CRITERIA FOR EVALUATION
OF
CATHOLIC ELEMENTARY
SCHOOLS

1965

Formulated and Edited by the Criteria Committee, Elementary School
Department of The National Catholic Educational Association

Comprises list of Committee Members and Consultants,
Instructional Blank, Manual, General Areas B, C, D, E,
F, G, H, I, J, K: Instructional Areas D 1-10, Statistical
Summary Section X, Graphic Summary Section Y.

THE CATHOLIC UNIVERSITY OF AMERICA PRESS
WASHINGTON, D. C. 20017

Nihil obstat:

Rt. Rev. Msgr. Joseph A. Gorham
Censor Deputatus

Imprimatur:

† Patrick A. O'Boyle
Archbishop of Washington

January 4, 1965

Criteria Publication Contributors

The following lists include the names of all personnel who assisted in the authorship of *Criteria for the Evaluation of Catholic Elementary Schools—1965* as workshop participants, committee members, area specialists or consultants.

STEERING COMMITTEE

Brother E. Anthony, F.S.C., Director
Sister Mary Richardine, B.V.M.

Sister Mary Nora, S.S.N.D.
Sister St. Regina Marie, C.N.D.

PARTICIPANTS IN THREE WORKSHOPS

Brother E. Anthony, F.S.C.
Sister Anna Mae, I.H.M.
Sister M. Celine, O.S.F.
Sister Mary Charlotte, O.S.B.
Mother M. Cornelia, O.S.B.
Sister Mary Dorothy, F.S.P.A.
Sister M. Edward, S.S.J.
Mother M. Eugene Joseph, S.S.J.
Sister Mary Florence, S.S.N.D.
Sister Mary Gemma, H.H.M.

Sister M. Jean Clare, O.P.
Sister Joan of Arc, I.H.M.
Sister Mary Lalande, I.H.M.
Sister M. Nicholas, C.S.J.
Sister Mary Nora, S.S.N.D.
Sister Mary Peter, O.P.
Sister Mary Richardine, B.V.M.
Sister Mary Sarah, S.C.L.
Sister Teresa George, S.C.N.
Sister M. Teresa, O.S.F.

PARTICIPANTS IN TWO WORKSHOPS

Mother M. Anastasia, I.B.V.M.
Sister Mary Elaine, S.S.N.D.
Sister Mary Gerard, O.S.F.
Sister Mary Laurietta, C.PP.S.
Sister Mary Leonella, C.S.C.

Sister Rita Dolores, S.N.D. de N.
Sister St. Mary Delphine, C.N.D.
Sister Mary St. Edgar, B.V.M.
Sister St. Regina Marie, C.N.D.
Mother M. Xavier, I.B.V.M.

PARTICIPANTS IN ONE WORKSHOP

Sister Anna Michael, C.S.J.
Sister M. Bernarda, C.PP.S.
Sister M. Damien, O.P.
Sister M. Esther, C.PP.S.
Sister M. Helen St. Paul, O.S.F.
Sister Hilda Marie, O.P.

Sister Irma Therese, S.P.
Sister Julie, S.N.D. de N.
Sister Maria del Carmen, C.R.S.M.
Sister Marie St. Aubyn, C.S.J.
Sister St. Catherine of Angels, C.N.D.

MEMBERS OF MUSIC COMMITTEE

Sister Cecilia, S.C.
Sister Cecilia Mary, S.C.
Sister Irene, S.C.
Sister Maria Magdalen, S.C.

Sister M. Muriel, S.C.
Sister Teresa Clare, S.C.
Sister M. Thecla, S.C.

MEMBERS OF ART COMMITTEE

Sister Adelaide, S.P.
Sister Esther, S.P.

Sister M. Irenita, O.S.F.
Sister Rose Michele, S.P.

AREA SPECIALISTS AND CONSULTANTS

Right Reverend Monsignor A. W. Behrens
Right Reverend Monsignor Irving A. DeBlanc
Right Reverend Monsignor Joseph A. Gorham
Right Reverend Monsignor Eugene Kevane
Very Reverend Monsignor Edgar P. McCarren
Brother Bernard Peter, F.S.C.
Brother Nicholas William, F.S.C.
Sister Aquinas, O.S.F.
Sister Mary Barbara, C.PP.S.
Sister Celine, O.S.B.
Sister Clara Francis, S.C.N.
Sister Mary de Lourdes, O.S.M.
Sister Mary Donald, S.C.
Sister Mary Dorita, B.V.M.
Sister Francis Regis, C.S.J.
Sister M. Hildegardis, C.S.C.

Sister M. Jerome, O.S.U.
Sister M. Johnice, I.H.M.
Sister Mary Leonide, C.S.S.J.
Sister Mary Linus, F.S.P.A.
Sister M. Lorenz, S.S.N.D.
Sister Margaret Dolores, S.N.D. de N.
Sister Marie Theresa, S.C.
Sister Maureen, O.S.U.
Sister Mary Nina, O.P.
Sister M. Paulina, S.C.
Sister Mary Ramon, O.P.
Sister Raymond de Jesus, F.S.E.
Sister Mary Ursula, R.S.M.
Gladys Anderson
Margaret E. Martignoni
Dorothy A. McGinniss

iii

Acknowledgments

The completion of *Criteria for the Evaluation of Catholic Elementary Schools—1965*, has been made possible primarily through the generosity of Religious Superiors who contributed thousands of dollars to finance travel and living expenses for the members of their Congregations who participated in the project.

Special acknowledgment is also due to the following persons:

RIGHT REVEREND MONSIGNOR JOSEPH A. GORHAM whose suggestion to Sister Mary Richardine, B.V.M., and to Sister Mary Nora, S.S.N.D., gave inspiration and impetus to the Criteria project;

RIGHT REVEREND MONSIGNOR JAMES A. MAGNER and to The Catholic University of America Press for authorization to undertake the revision of *Criteria for the Evaluation of Catholic Elementary Schools;*

RIGHT REVEREND MONSIGNOR FREDERICK G. HOCHWALT, Executive Secretary, and the staff of the National Catholic Educational Association, and to the NCEA Elementary School Department Executive Committee who gave continued support and encouragement to the project as a cooperative undertaking of the NCEA Elementary School Department and The Catholic University of America Press;

BROTHER D. JOHN, F.S.C., Provincial of the Baltimore Province of the Brothers of Christian Schools, who graciously made it possible for Brother E. Anthony to assume direction of the Criteria project;

National Study of Secondary School Evaluation for permission to use the format of the *Evaluative Criteria* given in correspondence with Roderic D. Matthews, Executive Secretary.

The Administration and Staff of Loretto Heights College and of the University of Dayton, Mother M. Cornelia, O.S.B., and the Sisters of the Benedictine Priory, Elizabeth, New Jersey, who provided facilities and assistance for the Criteria Workshops;

Diocesan Superintendents of Schools who shared expenses for a few workshop participants who are members of their diocesan school staffs;

Workshop participants, committee members, area specialists and consultants who gave generously of their time and talents in bringing the Criteria project to completion;

All those individuals who gave secretarial or clerical help in the preparation of the manuscript;

All those religious and lay persons whose prayerful assistance gave support to the Criteria project from its beginning to its culmination.

Steering Committee:

BROTHER E. ANTHONY, F.S.C.
SISTER MARY RICHARDINE, B.V.M.
SISTER MARY NORA, S.S.N.D.
SISTER ST. REGINA MARIE, C.N.D.

FOREWORD

The Catholic University of America began planning a set of evaluative criteria for Catholic elementary schools over twenty years ago. Between 1944 and 1948, graduate students of the Department of Education, working in seminars under the direction of Dr. T. George Foran, Sister Mary Vernice, S.N.D., and Rev. Joseph A. Gorham, formulated statements of criteria, tested their validity and reliability through application to schools in operation, and finally systematized them into a set which was published by The Catholic University of America Press in 1948 under the title *Criteria for the Evaluation of Catholic Elementary Schools*. A revised edition of this book was published in 1949.

In all, thirty-eight graduate students contributed to the 1948 edition. Seventeen of them were priests, of whom twelve are now diocesan superintendents of schools, one is the head of the Department of Religious Education at The Catholic University of America, two are high-school principals, and, unfortunately, two are now dead. Others in the seminars were sixteen Sisters, one Brother, two laymen, and two laywomen. Two of the Sisters are now college presidents, three are college teachers, and eleven are supervisors of elementary schools. The Brother now teaches at a Catholic university. One of the laymen is now an official in the Department of Education of the Province of Newfoundland; the other is associated with the New York City public school system. The present position of one of the laywomen is that of professor in a state teachers college, while the other is principal of a public elementary school. The subsequent success of its pioneer contributors attests to the talent which launched the project of which this present volume is its up-to-date form.

No less talented and, indeed, far more experienced in both education and evaluation are the contributors to this new publication. Assisting in the authorship of the volume were five priest-educators; three Brothers of the Christian Schools; seventy-three Sisters, representing twenty-seven different religious teaching communities in the United States and Canada; and three lay educators. In addition, hundreds of other Sister teachers contributed to its final form through participation in four workshops. The first workshop was held at Loretto Heights College, Denver, in 1963. The University of Dayton was the location for the second and third workshops in the summer of 1964. The fourth workshop, which was devoted to stylizing and editing, was held in the fall of 1964 at Ventnor, New Jersey, where the Benedictine Sisters made the facilities of their oceanfront retreat available to a group of about twenty persons who had been associated with the revisional project from its beginning. The manuscript submitted by this group was prepared for production by the staff of The Catholic University of America Press.

This is, perhaps, the most venturous project in which The Catholic University of America and the National Catholic Educational Association have cooperated. In the past the University and the Association have worked together on other projects important to Catholic education, but not of such far reaching influence as this one. With characteristic insight into Catholic education's problems and resolute solicitude for their solutions, the Right Reverend Monsignor Frederick G. Hochwalt, executive secretary of the N.C.E.A., lent the services of his staff to the project and with typical leadership rallied from diocesan and religious communities a cohort of collaborators in its behalf. Director of the project was Brother E. Anthony, F.S.C., evaluation consultant in the Secondary School Department of the Association. Brother Anthony was selected for this task because of his long experience on national committees concerned with evaluation. In the forties he served on committees organized by the Middle States Association of Colleges and Secondary Schools and wrote the D-16 section of the 1950 edition of *Evaluative Criteria;* through the fifties he worked on the National Study of Secondary School Evaluation's committees preparing the 1960 edition of *Evaluative Criteria* for four-year and senior high schools; and now in the sixties he is a member of the committees already at work preparing the 1970 edition of this work.

Educators familiar with the books of the National Study of Secondary School Evaluation will note a great likeness in format between *Evaluative Criteria* and *Criteria for Evaluation of Catholic Elementary Schools*. Permission to use the format of *Evaluative Criteria* was given by Dr. Roderic D. Matthews, executive secretary of the National Study of Secondary School Evaluation. Dr. Matthews, retired University of Pennsylvania professor of education and for many years a member of the Commission on Secondary Schools of the Middle States Association of Colleges and Secondary Schools, remembered the support Catholic high schools gave to the evaluation movement in its formative period of the thirties. At that time, when many schoolmen felt the use of the *Evaluative Criteria* too demanding of time and judgment in the evaluation of a high school, the late Right Reverend Monsignor John J. Bonner, then superintendent of schools of the Archdiocese of Philadelphia, offered Dr. Matthews several Catholic schools so that in their evaluation he could instruct groups of public school principals and teachers in the new procedures and demonstrate their value. The authors and editors of *Criteria for Evaluation of Catholic Elementary Schools* are grateful to Dr. Matthews for the advice and encouragement he has given them.

Responsible to a very great degree for completion of this volume are the Sisters who serve as associate and assistant secretaries of the Elementary School Department of the National Catholic Educational Association: Sister Mary Richardine, B.V.M., former associate secretary; Sister Mary Nora, S.S.N.D., present associate secretary, and Sister St. Regina Marie, C.N.D., present assistant secretary. These Sisters promoted and directed the four workshops out of which came the contents of this book. They have created interest in it by speaking about it wherever they went as representatives of the N.C.E.A., by writing about its value in the N.C.E.A.'s *Catholic Elementary Education News*, and by organizing workshops for the summer of 1965 throughout the country wherein Catholic educators may learn how to use it. Before any formal campaign for advanced orders was started, a dozen separate workshops had been organized and orders for over a thousand copies of the book had been received.

If it were not for the self-sacrificing spirit of Brother Anthony, of the three Sisters on the Steering Committee, and of all who participated in the workshops and acted as consultants, this project would not have been brought to the successful attainment this volume bespeaks. If the services of these teachers, supervisors, and administrators had had to be purchased, the book's pre-printing costs would have precluded any publisher's interest in it. Foundations sometimes help institutions in situations like this. The Carnegie Corporation helped bring the *Evaluative Criteria* of the National Study of Secondary School Evaluation into the service of schools; the General Education Board and the six regional accrediting associations provided funds for revisions. The only foundation which helped bring this volume into the service of Catholic elementary schools is the foundation of self-sacrifice.

Even with all the contributory service that brought this project to the printing phase, its resultant volume is an expensive one. The Catholic University of America Press has invested a considerable sum in its first printing. All associated with the project in any way are most grateful to the Right Reverend Monsignor James A. Magner, director of the Press, for the confidence he has in Catholic educators' acceptance of the fruit of their labors and for the cooperative manner in which he supported the project's development.

There is, perhaps, not a Catholic elementary school principal or teacher who has not at times wondered about the effectiveness of the program being offered in her school. Superintendents, too, have often reflected on the need of some method of evaluating their elementary schools and have sought some means of ascertaining just how effective they are. Designed primarily to assist superintendents, supervisors, principals, and teachers in assessing the educational endeavor of their schools, *Criteria for Evaluation of Catholic Elementary Schools* should also be provocative of specific improvements in Catholic education.

Joseph A. Gorham
School of Education
The Catholic University of America

Structure of Criteria Area Blank

The following statements are succinct points relating to each area. They are intended to clarify the structure of the specific sections of each area blank, namely, Guiding Principles; Instructions; Organization; Nature of Offerings; Physical Facilities; Direction of Learning: Instructional Staff, Instructional Activities, Instructional Materials, Methods of Evaluation.

Guiding Principles:

1. The statements included in this section spell out the general outline of the specific area or subject.
2. These statements consider the common and individual needs of students enrolled in the particular school.
3. Reference is made to specific techniques and resource materials utilized by this school.

Instructions:

1. Statements of Guiding Principles, Checklist items, and Evaluations may be modified to conform with the Philosophy and Objectives of the school being evaluated.
2. Under Comments explanation is given for changes consistent with stated Philosophy and Objectives and characteristics of the School and Community.
3. Minor differences in terminology should not be regarded as significant items of change.
4. Under Checklist items a code of letters is used to indicate varying degrees of the significance of specific items.
5. Evaluations represent numerical summations of the Checklist items.
6. A definite and consistent relationship exists between Checklist items and Evaluations.
7. Detailed instructions follow the statement of Guiding Principles in each area blank.

Organization:

1. The ways in which the program is organized in the school are indicated.
2. Reference is made to common and individual needs to be met.
3. The way in which the program meets these needs is stated.
4. Evidence is presented showing the use of research and available resource material.
5. Means for obtaining flexibility in organization are indicated.
6. Special techniques used by the school are specified.

Nature of Offerings:

1. The content of materials basic to the specific *Criteria* area is stressed.
2. A concern for common and individual needs of students is indicated.
3. Procedures for securing sequential development are pointed out.
4. Evidence of educational research techniques relating to the specific subject is cited.
5. Any experimental approaches are mentioned.

Physical Facilities:

1. The use of facilities common to the area is specified.
2. Special facilities and materials in use are enumerated.
3. Concern for the health and safety of the students is indicated.
4. Reference is made to quality and quantity of materials.

Direction of Learning:

This section is considered under four headings:

A. Instructional Staff
B. Instructional Activities
C. Instructional Materials
D. Methods of Evaluation

A. Instructional Staff:

1. Reference is made to the general education of staff members.
2. The specific preparation in the particular subject area being considered is indicated.
3. Professional experience, professional attitudes, and in-service work of the staff members are stressed.

B. Instructional Activities:

1. The ways in which instruction is given in light of objectives specified in Section B are indicated.
2. The common and individual needs of students as related to instruction are specified.
3. The logical development of procedures in attaining aims is pointed out.
4. Utilization of available facilities is weighed against actual achievement of school program.

C. Instructional Materials:

1. Materials available and in use in instructional procedures are listed.
2. Texts, reference materials, tools specific to the subject area, multi-sensory equipment, etc. are enumerated.

D. Methods of Evaluation:

In this section reference is made to the evaluation of instruction and student achievement through tests of various kinds, follow-up of graduates, surveys of parents and students, etc.

CRITERIA FOR EVALUATION
OF
CATHOLIC ELEMENTARY SCHOOLS

Table of Contents

Manual

Formulated and Edited by the Criteria Committee, Elementary School
Department of The National Catholic Educational Association

Evaluation of Elementary Schools

An effective school program includes evaluative procedures to determine the extent to which the school program is achieving the aims specified in the philosophy and objectives of the particular school. The validity of assuming that a school can be evaluated adequately in terms of its philosophy and objectives based on student need and the community served is attested in modern educational research. The projection of Criteria on the elementary level stems from the success of schools using similar Criteria on the secondary level.

Since the publication of the *1940 Evaluative Criteria for Secondary Schools*, Catholic schools of both diocesan and private sponsorship have found the procedure of self-evaluation a stimulating and effective means for self improvement. The subsequent revisions of the secondary Criteria in 1950 and 1960, the former with need for considerable modification, proved equally challenging to our personnel and schools. In view of this satisfaction with the Criteria on the secondary level of education, elementary administrators and staffs desired some similar means of evaluating their programs. Statements of standards had been developed on the elementary level by private and public agencies in individual states but no common publication similar to that developed by the Cooperative Study of Secondary School Standards was available. In 1944 the Education Department of the Catholic University of America undertook the compilation of a set of standards which might serve as criteria for the evaluation of Catholic elementary schools. Between 1944 and 1947 a seminar in elementary education at the University refined these standards and in 1948 the University published *Criteria for the Evaluation of Catholic Elementary Schools*. A revised edition published in 1949 was used in Catholic private and parochial elementary schools throughout the country.

During the 1960's several hundred requests for *Criteria for the Evaluation of Catholic Elementary Schools* were made to The Catholic University of America Press, indicating an awareness of the importance of elementary school evaluation on the part of administrators. In view of the changes taking place in educational patterns and programs, a revision of the 1949 edition of the Criteria was decided upon in February, 1963.

THE 1965 PUBLICATION

To publish criteria in keeping with present evaluation procedures a plan for revision was initiated between Right Reverend Monsignor Joseph A. Gorham of the Graduate Education Department of The Catholic University of America, and Sister Mary Richardine, B.V.M., Associate Secretary, and Sister Mary Nora, S.S.N.D., Assistant Secretary, of the Elementary School Department of the National Catholic Educational Association. It was decided to ask Brother E. Anthony, F.S.C., of the Department of Education of La Salle College, Philadelphia, Pennsylvania, and President of the NCEA Secondary School Department, to act as Director of the project. Brother Anthony was chosen for this work because of his experience as a member of the National Study of Secondary School Evaluation Committee which prepared the 1960 revision of *Evaluative Criteria*, a publication for use in secondary schools.

In the spring of 1963, preliminary meetings were conducted in Washington, D.C., at both the office of the National Catholic Educational Association and The Catholic University. Following these meetings, a third meeting was held at Kiel Auditorium, St. Louis, Missouri, in April, 1963 during the annual convention of the National Catholic Educational Association. A number of Catholic educators distinguished for their experience and leadership in elementary education were invited by Sister Mary Richardine to attend the St. Louis meeting and to participate in the Criteria project. This meeting resulted in the formulation of accepted procedures and the adoption of ideas for future work. A workshop was proposed for the summer of 1963.

LORETTO HEIGHTS COLLEGE CRITERIA WORKSHOP—1963

The first stage of the project was launched at Loretto Heights College, Denver, Colorado, during June, 1963. Brother Anthony, Director of the project, worked with the Criteria Committee, a group of thirty-four community and diocesan supervisors, elementary school principals, and college specialists from all sections of the country. A first draft of the proposed publication was made at the Loretto Heights Workshop.

The materials prepared at Loretto Heights College were edited and arranged in Criteria format by Brother Anthony and submitted to Sister Mary Richardine and Sister Mary Nora for criticism and analysis. These materials were then submitted to area specialists in the various fields of elementary education for review and recommendations. When these materials with critical reviews were returned to the office of the NCEA Elementary School Department, they were forwarded to the original subcommittee chairmen, who with the members of their respective committees considered the recommendations and obtained additional critiques from other educators. Each section was again revised according to the format suggested by the Director of the project.

Similar procedures were followed by fine arts specialists invited to organize sub-committees to prepare sections of the Criteria on Music and Art. Materials prepared by these committees were in turn submitted to the Criteria Committee and adapted to fit the total curricular pattern presented in the Criteria.

CRITERIA WORKSHOP—UNIVERSITY OF DAYTON, 1964

To complete the work done during 1963-64 a second workshop was proposed for the summer of 1964. A plan was submitted to Brother

Louis Faerber, S.M., Dean of the Graduate School of Education at the University of Dayton, Dayton, Ohio, for a three-week workshop to be offered from June 8 to 26, 1964.

The goal of this workshop in 1964 was to complete the writing of the Criteria, and to familiarize the Criteria Committee with the total project. At this stage of the project, additional area specialists assisted in the refinement of material in each area of the Criteria.

FOLLOW-UP WORKSHOPS

To supplement the work of refining and editing the Criteria, a follow-up workshop was conducted at the University of Dayton from June 29 to July 17, 1964 under the direction of Sister Mary Nora, S.S.N.D. This workshop was designed for Catholic elementary school superintendents, principals, and supervisors. Participants engaged in depth studies of the various sections of the Criteria. Rationale behind the workshop gave Catholic elementary school personnel familiarity with the Criteria as an instrument for evaluation of their individual schools and school systems.

Using recommendations of the participants in the second University of Dayton workshop, the Criteria Committee further refined the proposed publication. This final stage in the development of the Criteria project was accomplished during a workshop at the Ventnor residence of the Benedictine Sisters of Elizabeth, New Jersey, from September 4 to 11, 1964.

THE COMPLETED PROJECT

As previously stated, this project was initiated as a revision of the 1949 *Criteria for the Evaluation of Catholic Elementary Schools*. In preparing for the work, Brother Anthony received permission to adapt the format of *Evaluative Criteria* for the Catholic elementary school publication from Dr. Roderic Matthews, Executive Secretary, National Study of Secondary School Evaluation. *Criteria for the Evaluation of Catholic Elementary Schools—1965*, is a totally new publication both in format and content, instead of a revision of the 1949 edition, as originally planned.

EVALUATION PROCEDURES

A planned, professional self-evaluation of a school program or curriculum area by the staff of the school is a definite means for self-improvement and enrichment. This self-evaluation presumes the validity of the statement that a school should be guided by a *stated* philosophy of education and allied objectives, formulated to meet the needs of the student population and community which the school serves. The community for a Catholic school consists of the students enrolled in the school and their parents.

The materials presented in the CHECKLISTS and EVALUATIONS in the following Criteria forms have been prepared against a background of modern educational research by teachers and administrators of wide experience in elementary, secondary, and collegiate levels of education.

The items in the various sections are not intended to be construed as unalterable concepts. They are guides to help a staff formulate a reasonable analysis of the work being accomplished in a specific area of the school program. Under the heading of COMMENTS following the CHECKLISTS and EVALUATIONS, a school staff may explain any particular phases of the school program not included in the CHECKLIST items but which the school staff considers pertinent in that area.

The statements presented in the Criteria are, in the opinion of the personnel who constructed this instrument, significant factors in evaluating specific areas. It should not be expected that the suggestions made would be all-inclusive or totally accepted by all staffs. It is to be noted that the CHECKLIST items have a definite relationship with the EVALUATIONS listed below each CHECKLIST. The CHECKLIST items are answered by *letter* designation while EVALUATIONS are indicated numerically. (SEE INSTRUCTIONS FOR CHECKLIST AND EVALUATION SYMBOLS.)

Experience has proved that the value derived from the self-evaluation will depend upon the professional attitude evidenced by the school staff. Sufficient time must be allotted for staff meetings at which discussion should center around present conditions and practices weighed against intended objectives. It is recommended that a school spend at least a full year on a total school evaluation; however, the amount of time needed for a valid evaluation of individual areas of the program may differ.

This Criteria is not intended as an instrument of inspection. Its primary purpose is self-evaluation with an aim toward improvement and enrichment of the school program. Therefore, it would be helpful to a school staff to consult someone familiar with Criteria procedures who could explain significant aspects of a self-evaluation to the staff before the staff undertakes its work.

USE OF THE CRITERIA FOR CATHOLIC ELEMENTARY SCHOOLS

The Criteria may be used in a number of ways. Five specific uses are indicated here.

1.) Analysis of a particular subject area of the Program of Studies, i.e., English, Mathematics, etc.

2.) A study of a general area such as Administration, Guidance, etc.

3.) An evaluation of the total school program of an individual school.

4.) A diocesan study of comparative strengths and weaknesses in member schools.

5.) A survey by a Religious Community of one or more of its member schools.

Formulated and Edited by the Criteria Committee, Elementary School
Department of The National Catholic Educational Association

Philosophy and Objectives

GUIDING PRINCIPLES

A good school is one whose teachers know its purpose and use all available means to realize it. This knowledge of purpose constitutes the philosophy, the "why" of the school. Through the cooperative effort of the total school staff, a comprehensive philosophy is formulated which will give direction and purpose to the educational process and will provide for the complete education of every student.

A statement of philosophy must express clearly the position of the staff on such essentials as the nature of man and his supernatural destiny, the nature of truth both natural and revealed, and the relationship of the school to the home, the Church and the state. Recognition of these basic tenets must be evident in every area of the curricular and co-curricular program, in methods of instruction, in pupil-teacher relationships, in policies of administration, and in outcomes to be attained. Although requiring adaptation to changing times and circumstances, the essentials of Catholic education do not change since they are based on truth. The goals depend upon these essentials. The means of achieving these goals, however, will vary from school to school, depending upon individual needs and community resources.

Objectives are realistic, specific aims through which staff members strive to attain what is embodied in the stated philosophy. These objectives affect every administrative procedure and every learning experience in the school. Fulfillment of these objectives should enable students to meet the challenges of American democratic society as true Christians.

Each school evaluates itself in accord with its own philosophy and objectives. Every policy, every program, and every activity is studied in view of what the school has set itself to accomplish, and is judged in terms of what it is actually realizing. Evaluation is based primarily upon the extent to which the school fulfills its purpose in the light of its student population and the community it serves.

NAME OF SCHOOL_____ DATE_____

ADDRESS_____

(ARCH)DIOCESE OF_____

SELF-EVALUATION MEMBERS_____

_____

_____

I. The Statement of Philosophy

The expression of the school's philosophy embodies in general terms the ideals the school endeavors to achieve through its total program. Principles common to all Catholic elementary schools, as well as those principles determined by the unique conditions particular to a school, are included in the statement.

A recommended approach to the formulation of a statement of philosophy is to pose a series of questions which will provoke thought, stimulate discussion and clarification of principles, and effect a crystallization of ideas. The following questions are suggested for consideration by the staff.

1. What is the responsibility of the school in contributing to the total development of each student in terms of his origin, nature and destiny?

2. Does the school provide a balanced program maintaining a priority of objectives and a hierarchy of values?

3. Does the program reflect current knowledge of human growth and development?

4. Is adequate provision made for the identification of student needs at a given level, and for the successful achievement of related developmental needs?

5. Is the school committed to intellectual and cultural excellence?

6. Is the school committed to moral and spiritual excellence?

7. Is the school educating the student in the knowledge and skills necessary to prepare him for his place in life?

8. Is provision made in the program to develop potentialities of the students for creative thinking, for learning to accept responsibility, and for alert, active and articulate leadership?

9. Does teacher-student rapport reflect the teacher's consciousness of the dignity of the student created in God's image, redeemed in Christ, and a member of the Mystical Body?

10. Does the entire staff participate in the total program of education?

11. Is there evidence that creativity and experimentation are encouraged among the staff?

12. Does the co-curricular program reflect the philosophy of the school?

13. How does the school share responsibility with the home, the Church, the state, and other agencies in the total development of each student?

The preceding questions should stimulate the school staff to seek satisfactory answers and to pose further questions related specifically to the individual school situation. Advice and approval should be sought from the superintendent of schools, supervisors, and other qualified persons. The final expression of philosophy will be the result of cooperative thought and discussion among all members of the staff, and should be incorporated in the school handbook.

II. Statement of Objectives

The statement of objectives should express in specific terms the efforts of the school to meet the current needs and interests of its students in accordance with its philosophy. In preparing the statement, the staff should consult not only educational authorities and parents but also representative students, who should be given an opportunity to make known the interests and abilities of the student community. The objectives should be influenced by the following considerations:

1. The physical, emotional, intellectual, moral, and spiritual needs of each student as an individual and as a member of society.

2. The particular community in which the school is located.

3. The range of cultural, intellectual, social and economic background.

4. The needs of students in preparing for further education.

5. The availability of cultural resources and other educational agencies.

6. The obligation to prepare the student to give himself in service to God and to his fellowman.

7. Any other considerations which may be suggested by the statement of philosophy.

The objectives of the school implement in specific terms the ideals which are set down in the school's philosophy. All objectives must, in the final analysis, be made specific enough to serve as useful guides for judging educational practices and directing educational change. An example of a broad objective is: "Assumes responsibility for community living." A more specific objective is: "Observes community regulations for bicycle riders." Professional curriculum materials will be of assistance to the school staff in setting up objectives.

Section B presents a general overview of what the school is trying to achieve. Details of how this may be accomplished and how far the school has progressed will be found in later sections of the Criteria.

III. Procedures Followed in Development of Philosophy and Objectives

The procedures followed in arriving at a formulation of philosophy are of great significance. A philosophy which ensues from the combined efforts and thinking of the entire staff will be translated more readily into actual practice.

Indicate in your answers to the following questions the procedures used in developing the school's philosophy. Significant activities in the development of this philosophy should be noted.

1. Who prepared the statements in Parts I and II of Section B?

2. What procedures were followed in the development of the statements?

3. For how long a time did the staff work in developing the statements of philosophy and objectives?

4. What resource materials were used in preparing the statements of philosophy and objectives?

Formulated and Edited by the Criteria Committee, Elementary School
Department of The National Catholic Educational Association

School and Community

GUIDING PRINCIPLES

The Catholic elementary school exists primarily for the benefit of Catholic youth of the community or the group which it serves. This school community is a testing ground of religious understandings and practices.

Within the school community, ethnic groups differ in their inheritances of racial and national characteristics. The types of people vary in religious beliefs, in attitudes, and prejudices. Their present occupations and interests, as well as their hopes and prospects regarding the future, make for both diversity and similarity. It is essential that the personnel of the school have an understanding of the dynamics of the groups they serve and utilize their human and cultural resources.

A Catholic elementary school community is *primarily the students enrolled and their parents.* It may embrace the single concept of parochial, diocesan, private, and institutional or a combination of one or more of these concepts. Whatever its definition, every school community is interrelated with other communities and is a part of larger units such as the parish, diocese, city, state, nation, and world. Therefore, each school should apply its Catholic philosophy to its specific educational program within its own school community and to the more complex groups of which it is an integral part.

NAME OF SCHOOL_____ DATE_____

ADDRESS_____

(ARCH)DIOCESE OF_____

SELF-EVALUATION MEMBERS _____

_____

_____

©1965 by
The Catholic University of America Press, Inc., Washington, D. C. 20017

Explanation

A Catholic elementary school evaluation is based primarily on the extent to which *the needs* of the students enrolled in the school *are being met*. Since need is related to environmental resources and opportunities, it is necessary that the community as well as the student body be described. The goal is to give as complete a description as possible of the student body, the community or group served by the school, the opportunities for the young people and the hopes of their parents and friends. The school committee which fills in this section should not hesitate to extend or omit any tables or questions which seem incomplete or inappropriate in terms of their school or their community. The important obligation for all schools is to know *the nature and needs of the community*.

I. Basic Data Regarding Students

A. ENROLLMENT BY GRADES

1. In the space below enter data for current year (as of October 1) in the last division under CURRENT YEAR. Proceed from right to left entering data for each preceding year, with the first division at the left being used for the earliest year included. Enter data only for the grades in the school as organized, K to 8, 1 to 8, 1 to 6, etc.

GRADE	19—-19—			19—-19—			19—-19—			19—-19—			19—-19—			19—-19—			19—-19—			19—-19— (CURRENT YEAR)		
	B	G	Total	B	G	Total	B	G	Total	B	G	Total	B	G	Total	B	G	Total	B	G	Total	B	G	Total
8th																								
7th																								
6th																								
5th																								
4th																								
3rd																								
2nd																								
1st																								
Kdg.																								
Spec.																								
Total																								

2. Describe any studies which have been made regarding the progress of a group of students who entered the lowest grade at the same time.

3. Do you consider the distribution of enrollments satisfactory? If not, explain.

B. AGE-GRADE DISTRIBUTION OF STUDENTS

Age in Years as of October 19____

Grade	5	5½	6	6½	7	7½	8	8½	9	9½	10	10½	11	11½	12	12½	13	13½	14	14½	15	15½	16	16½	Total
K																									
1																									
2																									
3																									
4																									
5																									
6																									
7																									
8																									
Spec.																									

1. Describe any uses of the above information which are made regularly or which have been made during the past three years.

2. What factors within the school or community explain any deviation from normal which are revealed by these data?

3. What provisions are being made for students who deviate in age from normal grade placement?

C. MENTAL ABILITY

On the form below, list the number of students in either the I.Q. or percentile ranges if intelligence or mental ability test records are available.

| RANGE | | GRADE ONE | GRADE TWO | GRADE THREE | GRADE FOUR | GRADE FIVE | GRADE SIX | GRADE SEVEN | GRADE EIGHT | TOTAL | |
I.Q.	Percentile									Number	Per cent
Total											
Year tests were given											

Fill in the form below.

GRADE LEVEL	NAME OF TEST	FORM

What provisions are made for students who score markedly above or below the norm? List other programs of mental ability testing administered within the last three years.

D. STABILITY

1. Indicate on the following form the number of years which each student *of the highest grade* has been in *this* school.

NUMBER OF YEARS IN THIS SCHOOL (INCLUDING THE PRESENT YEAR)	MEMBERS OF THE HIGHEST GRADE			
	Boys	Girls	TOTAL	
			Number	Per cent
1				
2				
3				
4				
5				
6				
7				
8				
9				
10 or more				
Total				

2. Indicate on the following form the number of students *of the highest grade* who have attended the number of schools specified in the column headings. Include this school.

TYPE OF SCHOOL	NUMBER OF SCHOOLS OR MORE						
	1	2	3	4	5	6	7+
Elementary							
Junior High							
Special							

3. Indicate on the following form the years of service of your faculty in this school in the current year.

FACULTY	YEARS OF SERVICE IN THIS SCHOOL					
	1–3	4–6	7–9	10–14	15–19	20+
Lay						
Religious						

4. What provision does the school make for gathering data for these forms?

5. What unusual conditions are revealed by this survey?

6. What environmental factors contribute to any unsatisfactory conditions revealed by this survey?

7. What provisions are being made to improve them?

8. List each receiving junior and senior high school to which you send students, and show the number of students sent and the grade level at which they were admitted this fall. (Attach sheet, if necessary.)

COMMENTS

E. WITHDRAWALS

1. Indicate in the form below the major reason for withdrawal. Do not count any student more than once. The number of students should include all who have withdrawn from school during the twelve months preceding the opening of the current school year.

REASON FOR WITHDRAWAL	BOYS	GIRLS	TOTAL	
			Number	Per cent of total enrollment of school
1. Transferred to another school with change of residence				
2. Transferred without change of residence				
3. Program of studies				
4. Poor scholarship				
5. Lack of interest in school				
6. Illness of student				
7. Disciplinary difficulties				
8. Emotional disturbance				
9. Financial reasons				
10. Others:				
11. Unknown				
Total				

2. What provisions are being made to gather the above information regularly?

3. What unusual conditions are revealed by this survey?

4. What environmental factors contribute to any unsatisfactory conditions which are revealed by this survey?

5. What provisions are being made to eliminate unnecessary withdrawals?

F. EDUCATIONAL INTENTIONS

1. In what year of the student's school life is he questioned about future formal education?

2. Does the school make available to the student and the parents information relating to educational opportunities on the secondary level?

3. Is the information specified above organized and kept up-to-date?

4. In general, what are the educational intentions of eighth grade students attending this school?

5. Parallel the desires of the students with available educational advantages.

6. Does the school make opportunity for the exceptionally gifted student to progress according to his ability?

7. What provisions are made to meet the needs of other exceptional students, such as the physically and mentally handicapped?

8. Does the school maintain close articulation with secondary schools which students attend?

9. To what extent are the above data (or additional data) used in planning individual and group educational programs?

II. Basic Data Regarding the Community

A. POPULATION DATA FOR THE SCHOOL COMMUNITY

Year to which this information applies: 19_____

1. Define the boundaries of your school community.

2. Estimate total population (include adults) of the school community ...._____

3. Estimate the total number of elementary school children of your parish who attend a public grade school.._____

4. Estimate the total number of elementary school children in your school community._____

5. If a parish school, do you admit students from other parishes to your school?....._____

6. Do you admit non-Catholic students?_____ Number:_____(19_____)

7. Total number of elementary schools of all types in your area ...._____

8. Student population of this school..._____

9. What per cent—if any—of students come from rural areas?..............._____

10. What studies are being undertaken by the school relative to enrollment conditions?

B. OCCUPATIONAL STATUS OF ADULTS

State the type of adult occupation prevalent in the school community.

C. EDUCATIONAL STATUS OF ADULTS

State the approximate number of years of academic learning of parents.

D. EDUCATIONAL GOALS OF THE STUDENTS

Estimate the number and per cent of eighth graders whose educational goals are indicated under each of the following categories:

1. Catholic high school _____ _____

2. Public high school _____ _____

3. College prep course _____ _____

4. Major seminary _____ _____

5. School for aspirants _____ _____

6. Vocational arts _____ _____

7. Business education _____ _____

8. Others: (specify) _____

_____

E. FINANCIAL RESOURCES

1. Explain the procedures by which this school is financed. (Attach summary statement; if desired.)

2. Does this school operate on a budget system?............................._____

F. TRANSPORTATION

1. What per cent of students are transported at public expense? ...._____

2. What per cent of students are transported by public service? ...._____

3. What per cent of students are transported by parish bus at parental expense?....._____

4. What per cent of students are transported by parish bus at parish expense?......._____

5. What per cent of students are transported by car pool?......................_____

G. COMPOSITION OF THE COMMUNITY

Elaborate on pertinent features of the community which influence the school program such as religion, bilinguality, socio-economic background, interrelating cultures, and changing population.

III. Community Agencies

The following items may be answered as applying to the school's neighborhood or as agencies actually used by this school regardless of their location. A comprehensive list of all possible resources is not sought in this section—list those agencies which are affecting education in this school.

Every Catholic elementary school has the responsibility to inculcate into the lives of its students an understanding of the common brotherhood of man and the practice of the spiritual and corporal works of mercy. The development of qualities of sacrifice, generosity, and service is basic to a complete Christian educational program.

A. RELIGIOUS AND APOSTOLIC AGENCIES

_____ 1. Propagation of the Faith

_____ 2. Archconfraternity of the Holy Childhood

_____ 3. The Sodality of Our Lady

_____ 4. Catholic Students Mission Crusade

_____ 5. Junior Holy Name

_____ 6. Junior Legion of Mary

_____ 7. Dominic Savio Club

_____ 8. Young Catholic Students

_____ 9. Vocation Clubs

_____ 10. Eucharistic Crusade

_____ 11. Parish Organizations (list)

_____ 12. Others

COMMENTS

B. EDUCATIONAL AGENCIES

1. *Public library* or *library branch*

Name _____

Check when library services are available:

	Sunday	Monday	Tuesday	Wednesday	Thursday	Friday	Saturday
Morning							
Afternoon							
Evening							

   a) If the community served by this elementary school has a local library or library branch:
     (1) Indicate what percentage of the students have public library cards................ _____
     (2) Indicate what percentage of the adult members of the families have public library
        cards .... _____

   b) In the list below check the sources of books used by the people in the community served by this school:

     _____ Parish libraries

     _____ County library service

     _____ Bookmobile

     _____ State library service

     _____ College or university library

     _____ Other free libraries

     _____ Rental library

     _____ Other libraries (Describe)

2. *Other elementary schools*

3. *High schools*

4. *Industrial and vocational schools*

B. EDUCATIONAL AGENCIES—*Continued*

5. *Collegiate institutions*

6. *Seminaries and schools for aspirants*

7. *Museums, art galleries, planetarium, botanical gardens, zoological gardens, NASA exhibition buildings, etc.*

8. *Youth serving agencies,* such as C.Y.O., Cub-scouts, Brownies, Boy Scouts, Girl Scouts, Campfire Girls, etc.

COMMENTS

C. RECREATIONAL OPPORTUNITIES

It is the community responsibility to offer adequate recreational opportunities to young and old. The school cooperates with the community in upgrading television, motion pictures, and radio programs. It also assists local agencies in developing wholesome and well-supervised places of recreation.

Under these headings, list the services found in your community:

1. *Public recreational facilities*

_____ Parks

_____ Athletic fields

_____ Playgrounds

_____ Swimming pools

_____ Camps

_____ Clubs

_____ Bicycling

_____ Hiking

Others

_____

_____

2. *Diocesan and parish facilities*

_____ Centers

_____ Catholic youth organizations

_____ Dramatic societies

_____ Music organizations

_____

_____

3. *Other recreational agencies*

_____ Scouts

_____ Kiwanis Club

_____ Theaters

_____

COMMENTS

D. CIVIC ORGANIZATIONS

The staff of the school should be familiar with the various agencies active in the community.

1. *Community agencies*

   _____ Parent-teacher organizations

   _____ Youth Council

   _____ Chamber of Commerce

   _____ _____

   _____ _____

   _____ _____

COMMENTS

2. *Social service agencies*

   _____ Catholic Charities

   _____ United Fund

   _____ Catholic Youth Service Bureau

   _____ National Catholic Welfare Conference

   _____ _____

   _____ _____

   _____ _____

COMMENTS

3. *Religious organizations*

   _____ Holy Name Society

   _____ Serra Club

   _____ Teresians

   _____ _____

   _____ _____

   _____ _____

COMMENTS

4. *Racial or ethnic organizations*

   _____ Interracial groups

   _____ Citizens for Educational Freedom

   _____ _____

   _____ _____

   _____ _____

COMMENTS

D. CIVIC ORGANIZATIONS—*Continued*

5. *Service Clubs*

_____ Kiwanis Club

_____ Rotary Club

_____ _____

_____ _____

_____ _____

COMMENTS

6. *Other, such as business organizations, cultural organizations, professional organizations, patriotic societies, etc.*

_____ _____

_____ _____

_____ _____

_____ _____

_____ _____

_____ _____

E. HEALTH AND SANITATION FACILITIES

If the health and sanitation facilities are satisfactory in serving your school community, check the following:

1. _____ a well organized health department

2. _____ sufficient and accessible hospital services

3. _____ child guidance clinics

4. _____ sufficient and available medical and dental services

5. _____ efficient nursing services

6. _____ regular testing service for water purification

7. _____ adequate provisions for sewage and refuse disposal

8. _____ adequate inspection of milk and food supply

COMMENTS

IV. Procedures

What procedures were used in conducting this survey?

Formulated and Edited by the Criteria Committee, Elementary School
Department of The National Catholic Educational Association

Curriculum

GUIDING PRINCIPLES

The elementary school curriculum consists of all the experiences of the students under the direction of the school personnel. In this particular Section D, emphasis is placed on the curriculum as it functions through programs of studies, supplementary curricular activities, and all the other guided learning experiences of the students.

The curriculum is structured to develop proper attitudes, habits, and values. This is intended to prepare the students to live in a complex American society and ultimately to attain their eternal destiny.

The curriculum includes the basic subject skills and learnings and is flexible enough to provide for individual differences and needs. Specialized programs for the gifted and remedial instruction are integral parts of the curriculum.

The scope of the curriculum should be broad enough to allow for improvement and flexible enough to incorporate new developments and techniques.

Ideally, the staff of each school within a system should be fully and personally involved both in the development of the curriculum and in the planning of supplementary curricular activities. In constructing the curriculum the staff uses research findings, school surveys, and community resources.

For successful implementation and articulation of the curriculum it is important to try to include representative consultants, high school teachers, principals, psychologists, and education administrators.

To ensure continuous improvements there is a periodic re-examination of the curriculum by an evaluative committee.

NAME OF SCHOOL_____ DATE_____

ADDRESS_____

(ARCH)DIOCESE OF_____

SELF-EVALUATION MEMBERS_____

_____

_____

Instructions

When undertaking a self-evaluation the members of the school staff should use the statement of GUIDING PRINCIPLES and CHECKLIST items as an aid to determining the extent to which their school program coincides with the Philosophy and Objectives of the school and meets the needs of the school population and community served. Of necessity a staff will modify statements of Guiding Principles, Checklist items and Evaluations to conform with the philosophy and characteristics of the particular school doing the evaluation. Wherever changes are made the school should explain under Comments the reasons for the change in relation to its own program. Minor differences in terminology should not be regarded as significant items of change.

CHECKLISTS

Checklist items consist of statements deemed applicable to the area of the Criteria being evaluated. These are suggested ideas and are not to be interpreted as the only statements applicable to the area or as all-inclusive. A school may wish to add additional statements of its own that will explain further the particular program of the school. Space is provided in each Checklist for such additions. If the change is regarded as significant, the school will use the letter C in the Checklist as indicated in the following instructions and explain under Comments the precise nature of its offerings.

A staff should note that a definite relation pertains between Checklist items and Evaluations. Members of the staff should familiarize themselves with the definite meanings of Checklist symbols and Evaluation ratings.

CHECKLIST items may be indicated as follows:

E—The statement or condition is *extensive* in application.

M—The statement or condition is *moderately* achieved.

L—The statement or condition is limited in application.

MN—The condition is missing but judged needed by the staff.

N—The condition does not apply to this school.

*C—The condition is achieved in a manner different from Checklist items.

  * Wherever C is used, this aim should be stated in one of the additional numbers of the Checklist and explained under COMMENTS.

EVALUATIONS

Evaluations represent numerical summations of the Checklist items. The rating is determined from discussions of the staff as related to the consistency of the school program with stated Philosophy and Objectives.

To secure a composite view of the school's outcomes in each area of the Criteria, a school will project the Evaluation ratings to the X Blank of the respective areas. A further picture of the total program will be secured by tabulating the Average of the X Blank on the Graphic Summary provided in the Y Blank. Instructions for such procedure are listed in the X and Y Blanks.

Evaluations are indicated as follows:

5—The condition is excellent and extensive. (Please note that 5 does not mean "perfect.")

4—The condition is very good. A school may care to use a further refinement of 4a or 4b: 4a indicates that the condition is extensive and functioning well; 4b indicates that the condition is moderately extensive but functioning excellently.

3—The condition meets student needs to a reasonable degree.

2—The condition is in need of *achievable* improvement.

1—The condition is not being achieved and its need is not recognized.

*MN—The condition is missing but needed.

*N—The condition does not apply.

* When MN or N are accepted by the staff for an *Evaluation* rating the divisor on the X Blank must be adjusted accordingly. N should not be used in CHECKLISTS and EVALUATIONS unless the condition absolutely DOES NOT APPLY. If the item is educationally desirable the school should not use N simply because it does not make use of the item. An adequate replacement for the item may fulfill the conditions of the Checklist.

I. Organization

The Curriculum:

( ) 1. is based upon the objectives of the school; it is rooted in a philosophy which recognizes the child in his fundamental relationships to God, fellowmen, self and nature.

( ) 2. is based upon an understanding of the total nature of the child.

( ) 3. provides for the common and individual needs of students.

( ) 4. includes specialized programs for gifted students.

( ) 5. includes specialized programs for slow-learners.

( ) 6. makes provision for remedial instruction.

( ) 7. incorporates a balanced program of sequentially-developed unifying concepts in the various subject areas.

( ) 8. is flexible in time allotments in order to provide for varied needs of the students.

( ) 9. can be adapted to new methodology and techniques.

( ) 10. provides activities to meet intellectual, physical, emotional, social, and spiritual needs of students.

( ) 11. emphasizes the importance of student participation in learning activities.

( ) 12. gives evidence of having been re-examined from time to time to provide for improvement.

( ) 13. is directed toward articulation with the programs of other elementary and secondary schools within the community.

( ) 14.

( ) 15.

EVALUATIONS

( ) a. *How well does the program provide for the development of the total nature of the child?*

( ) b. *How well is the curriculum adapted to meet the needs of different levels of ability?*

( ) c. *How balanced is the curriculum in scope, sequence, and time allotments?*

( ) d. *To what extent is provision made for improvement in the curriculum?*

COMMENTS

II. Curriculum Development Procedures

Included within curriculum development procedures are those initiated or carried on within the school itself as well as those stemming from other agencies. These agencies include parent-teacher associations, parish and diocesan school boards, town, district, city, and state agencies *only when these assist in the development of school curriculum.*

The checklist and evaluations of this area consider all these procedures.

CHECKLIST

( ) 1. Curriculum procedures are developed on the basis of student and community needs, in accordance with a Christian philosophy of life.

( ) 2. Staff members teaching on the same level are encouraged to discuss and coordinate plans, improvements, and procedures and are allotted the needed time.

( ) 3. Staff members teaching on different levels are encouraged to discuss and coordinate plans, improvements, and procedures and are allotted the needed time.

( ) 4. The curriculum evolves from the thinking and solicited contribution of *each* member of the school staff.

( ) 5. Teachers are relieved of classroom teaching at specified times to participate in the construction of the curriculum.

( ) 6. In the development of the curriculum, the suggestions of students, both past and present, are considered.

( ) 7. Professional guidance is solicited in developing specific areas of the curriculum.

( ) 8. The opinions of parents are considered in the development of the curriculum.

( ) 9. Financial aid is available to defray necessary expenses of curriculum projects, textbooks, reference materials, and secretarial assistance.

( ) 10. The curriculum is articulated with the offerings of other school systems.

( ) 11. In-service education in curriculum construction is provided.

( ) 12. In-service education is financed by the various agencies involved in setting up the curriculum.

( ) 13.

( ) 14.

Techniques for developing and improving the curriculum include:

( ) 15. a follow-up study of student performance at the secondary level.

( ) 16. analysis of probable causes of student failure in the elementary school.

( ) 17. utilization of research reports and surveys on a local, state and/or national level.

( ) 18. reference to materials produced by diocesan, city, state, regional and national organizations for curriculum improvements.

( ) 19. use of other local community resources.

( ) 20. periodic re-examination of the curriculum.

( ) 21.

( ) 22.

EVALUATIONS

( ) a. *To what degree do curriculum development techniques show awareness of the needs of students and community?*

( ) b. *How extensively has the staff participated in the development of the curriculum?*

( ) c. *To what degree are curriculum materials and professional resources available?*

( ) d. *To what degree are curriculum materials and professional resources used?*

COMMENTS

III. Subject Offerings

A. EXTENT OF SUBJECT OFFERINGS

If there are subjects which cannot be classified according to this table, write them in the blank headings. When the titles used in the table do not adequately represent the subjects offered, make the appropriate changes. Include only offerings which are a regular part of the school's program of studies. Do not include here activities which are evaluated in Section E, "Student Activity Program."

	SUBJECT FIELD	KEY	KDGN.	GRADE 1	GRADE 2	GRADE 3	GRADE 4	GRADE 5	GRADE 6	GRADE 7	GRADE 8
	ART	E									
		CS									
		MW									
		WY									
		FT									
		PT									
		ST									
ENGLISH LANGUAGE ARTS	ENGLISH	E									
		CS									
		MW									
		WY									
		FT									
		PT									
		ST									
	HAND-WRITING	E									
		CS									
		MW									
		WY									
		FT									
		PT									
		ST									
	READING	E									
		CS									
		MW									
		WY									
		FT									
		PT									
		ST									
	SPELLING	E									
		CS									
		MW									
		WY									
		FT									
		PT									
		ST									
	FOREIGN LANGUAGES	E									
		CS									
		MW									
		WY									
		FT									
		PT									
		ST									

Key: E—Enrollment   MW—Minutes per week   FT—Full-time Teachers
         CS—Class Size   WY—Weeks per year   PT—Part-time Teachers
                                                       ST—Special Teachers

	Subject Field	Key	Kdgn.	Grade 1	Grade 2	Grade 3	Grade 4	Grade 5	Grade 6	Grade 7	Grade 8
SOCIAL STUDIES	GEOGRAPHY	E									
		CS									
		MW									
		WY									
		FT									
		PT									
		ST									
	HISTORY & CIVICS*	E									
		CS									
		MW									
		WY									
		FT									
		PT									
		ST									
	HEALTH, SAFETY, PHYSICAL EDUCATION	E									
		CS									
		MW									
		WY									
		FT									
		PT									
		ST									
	MATHE-MATICS	E									
		CS									
		MW									
		WY									
		FT									
		PT									
		ST									
	MUSIC	E									
		CS									
		MW									
		WY									
		FT									
		PT									
		ST									
	RELIGION	E									
		CS									
		MW									
		WY									
		FT									
		PT									
		ST									
	SCIENCE	E									
		CS									
		MW									
		WY									
		FT									
		PT									
		ST									

Key: E—Enrollment MW—Minutes per week FT—Full-time Teachers
CS—Class Size WY—Weeks per year PT—Part-time Teachers
ST—Special Teachers

* Check here if Social Studies is an integrated program.

ADDITIONAL OFFERINGS (Indicate below)

SUBJECT FIELD	KEY	KDGN.	GRADE 1	GRADE 2	GRADE 3	GRADE 4	GRADE 5	GRADE 6	GRADE 7	GRADE 8
	E									
	CS									
	MW									
	WY									
	FT									
	PT									
	ST									
	E									
	CS									
	MW									
	WY									
	FT									
	PT									
	ST									

Key:
E—Enrollment
CS—Class Size
MW—Minutes per week
WY—Weeks per year
FT—Full-time Teachers
PT—Part-time Teachers
ST—Special Teachers

COMMENTS *(on Subject Offerings or Special Offerings)*

A. EXTENT OF SUBJECT OFFERINGS—Continued

SUPPLEMENTARY MATERIALS

The following are available:

1. a copy of the curriculum and programs of study.
2. a copy of administrative handbook.
3. a statement of policy concerning the curriculum and specialized offerings geared to individual differences.
4. a complete daily time schedule for the program at each level.
5. a time schedule for the use of multi-sensory and library materials.
6. a time schedule for the use of special facilities and services such as cafeteria, gymnasium, auditorium, and bus. transportation.
7. a copy of the school calendar.

EVALUATIONS

(   )   *a. How adequate are the subject offerings in terms of the educational needs?*
(   )   *b. How extensive are materials outlining accepted policies?*
(   )   *c. To what extent do time schedules meet educational needs?*

COMMENTS

B. GENERAL CHARACTERISTICS OF CURRICULUM

(Basic subjects are listed in this section. Special offerings are considered under the sub-sections related to their subject areas.)

CHECKLIST

The curriculum includes:

(   ) 1. instruction and activities designed to educate the students for spiritual, mental, emotional, social, and physical growth.

(   ) 2. a developmental study of religious truths and of Sacred Scripture, participation in worship, practice in Christ-like living and growth in self knowledge.

(   ) 3. a variety of experiences for developing skills in the language arts (listening, speaking, reading and creative writing).

(   ) 4. activities directed toward the use of correct grammar, spelling, and vocabulary.

(   ) 5. an appreciation of good literature.

(   ) 6. the development of legible and neat handwriting.

(   ) 7. content which emphasizes concepts, skills and structure of mathematics.

(   ) 8. knowledge and appreciation of animal and plant life, the earth, and the universe.

(   ) 9. experiences designed to help students interpret historical and geographic facts and concepts.

(   ) 10. stress on American culture and citizenship as well as an understanding and appreciation of other cultures.

(   ) 11. a well-articulated program of foreign language study.

(   ) 12. knowledge, appreciation, and skills in music and arts.

(   ) 13. a program of health, safety, physical education and organized games intended to develop physical fitness and sportsmanship.

(   ) 14. an effective guidance program.

(   ) 15. activities which aid the students to work harmoniously with others and to exert effective leadership.

(   ) 16. preparation of students for proper use of leisure time.

(   ) 17. a variety of experiences and activities that will encourage critical and creative thinking.

(   ) 18. provision for varying interests and abilities of students.

(   ) 19. adequate articulation of subject offerings with other school systems.

(   ) 20.

(   ) 21.

EVALUATIONS

(   ) *a. How successful is the curriculum in developing correct attitudes, ideals, understandings, and habits?*

(   ) *b. How appropriate is the choice of subject offerings in the curriculum in terms of common needs of students?*

(   ) *c. How appropriate is the choice of subject offerings in the curriculum in terms of the particular needs of individual students?*

(   ) *d. To what degree do the staff and administration assume responsibility for developing and maintaining basic skills in curriculum areas?*

COMMENTS

C. INSTRUCTIONAL ACTIVITIES

CHECKLIST

(   ) 1. Instruction is aimed toward the achievement of comprehensive but specific goals in each of the subject areas, and coordinated with the objectives of the school.

(   ) 2. Individual needs of students are provided for in specialized programs through various types of grouping and organizational patterns.

(   ) 3. Instruction demonstrates meaningful and adequate preparation of materials.

(   ) 4. Good rapport and cooperation of the staff is evidenced by a correlated and integrated program.

(   ) 5. Programs are enriched by the effective use of community resources.

(   ) 6. The library functions as an integral part of the program.

(   ) 7. Provision is made for modification of instructional activities.

(   ) 8. The program of instructional activities is articulated with the offerings of secondary schools in the locality.

(   ) 9.

(   ) 10.

EVALUATIONS

(   ) a. *How extensive is the relationship of the instructional activities to the specific subject areas and the objectives of the school?*

(   ) b. *How satisfactory are instructional activities in fulfilling the needs of students?*

(   ) c. *How extensively are varied instructional materials used?*

(   ) d. *To what extent is good rapport and cooperation of the staff in evidence in the curriculum?*

(   ) e. *How extensively are community resources utilized?*

(   ) f. *How successfully do instructional activities articulate with secondary school offerings?*

COMMENTS

D. METHODS OF EVALUATION

Summaries of the general characteristics of the methods of evaluation in all the areas of the curriculum are included in this Section. Evaluative procedures pertinent to specific subject areas are treated in the sub-sections related to those fields.

CHECKLIST

( ) 1. Evaluation of the achievement of the entire class and individual students is important in the teaching-learning process.

( ) 2. Students are encouraged to evaluate their own progress in learning.

( ) 3. Evaluation results are utilized in curriculum planning.

( ) 4. The validity and usefulness of standardized tests are examined to determine their value.

( ) 5. Standardized tests, teacher-made tests, and a variety of other testing techniques are employed.

( ) 6. Strengths and weaknesses of the curriculum are identified through testing.

( ) 7. Follow-up studies of the achievements of graduates are used to estimate the effectiveness of the curriculum.

( ) 8.

( ) 9.

EVALUATIONS

( ) a. *How successfully do evaluative procedures identify the abilities of students?*

( ) b. *How effective are evaluative procedures in helping students to identify their strengths and weaknesses?*

( ) c. *How adequately are evaluative results interpreted, analyzed, and utilized for the improvement of teaching techniques and methods?*

( ) d. *To what extent do evaluative procedures reveal the effectiveness of the curriculum?*

( ) e. *To what extent are follow-up studies of graduates appropriate and satisfactory?*

COMMENTS

IV. General Outcomes of the Curriculum

In measuring the effectiveness of the curriculum, it is important that the staff be concerned with evidence gathered from checklists and evaluative items. Yet, it is inevitable that evaluation of general outcomes may be difficult because there are vital factors which cannot be measured. However, some outcomes can be made meaningful and informative by the use of follow-up studies of former students and graduates.

In the light of information gathered from a school evaluation, school personnel often know what factors should be emphasized in parent-teacher conferences, student interviews, and faculty meetings. There are other evaluative outcomes, however, which will only result from observation and personal judgment on the part of the staff.

CHECKLIST

Observations and accumulated evidence by staff members show that students:

(   ) 1. develop a sense of spiritual and moral values.

(   ) 2. demonstrate integrity and honesty in school activities.

(   ) 3. are developing self-reliance in decision-making and in seeing plans through to completion.

(   ) 4. are willing to sacrifice time and personal interests to assist others.

(   ) 5. will acknowledge personal failure or inadequacy and assume responsibility for their actions and obligations.

(   ) 6. recognize the rights of others and are willing to defend courteously these rights in the cause of justice and integrity.

(   ) 7. respect the dignity of all peoples regardless of race, color, nationality, economic background or religious affiliation.

(   ) 8. utilize time and abilities well.

(   ) 9. exercise effective leadership and work harmoniously with others.

(   ) 10. have a spirit of sportsmanship in school activities.

(   ) 11. respect ecclesiastical and civil authority.

(   ) 12. speak respectfully and considerately of parents and other members of the family.

(   ) 13. progress satisfactorily in basic subject areas.

(   ) 14. show competence in special areas of the curriculum.

(   ) 15. show responsibility in caring for school property.

(   ) 16. participate in the social and cultural life of the community.

(   ) 17. develop an aesthetic sense in the presence of beauty.

(   ) 18. exhibit creativity and originality in classroom situations and school activities.

(   ) 19. engage in physical fitness activities.

(   ) 20. manifest willingness to comply with safety rules and regulations.

(   ) 21.

(   ) 22.

A follow-up study of graduates shows that students:

(   ) 23. have gained admission to the secondary schools of their choice.

(   ) 24. are succeeding in the secondary schools.

(   ) 25. participate in activities of the secondary school, parish, and community.

(   ) 26.

(   ) 27.

EVALUATIONS

(   ) a. *To what extent do observations and evaluative results show that present students are achieving goals suggested in the general outcomes stated above?*

(   ) b. *To what extent do observations and evaluative results show that former students and graduates are achieving goals suggested in the general outcomes stated above?*

COMMENTS

V. Special Characteristics of the Curriculum

1. What aspects of the curriculum are most adequate and effective?

   a.

   b.

   c.

2. What aspects of the curriculum need adaptation, change, or improvement?

   a.

   b.

   c.

3. What aspects of the curriculum evidence a recent re-examination and evaluation in terms of new trends and the use of modern instructional devices?

   a.

   b.

   c.

4. Within the last three years, what steps have been taken to study and improve the curriculum, program of study, and professional education of the staff?

   a.

   b.

   c.

5. Discuss tentative plans for improvement of the curriculum, the program of study, and the professional preparation of the staff.

VI. General Evaluation of Curriculum

EVALUATIONS

(   ) a. To what extent is the curriculum consistent with the philosophy and objectives given in Section B?
(   ) b. To what extent does the curriculum meet the needs of students indicated in Section C?
(   ) c. To what extent is the school identifying problems in the curriculum and seeking their solution?

Formulated and Edited by the Criteria Committee, Elementary School
Department of The National Catholic Educational Association

Art

GUIDING PRINCIPLES

The over-all objective of art instruction is the advancement of all pupils in sensitivity, skill, and appreciation. There should be observable evidence that its influence is felt by faculty and students.

Art activities in the elementary school develop the basic principles of art and lay the foundation for appreciation by introducing the students to standards of value and achievement relative to the various levels of maturity. They develop skills and insights that will help the students become aware of the relationship of art to daily living.

The instructional program provides a means for all students to develop an appreciation of aesthetic values, a skill in self-expression, and a knowledge of our art heritage. The function of art is to sensitize the individual, as stated in the words of Pius XII, "to open a window to the infinite for his hungry soul."

NAME OF SCHOOL_____ DATE_____

ADDRESS_____

(ARCH)DIOCESE OF_____

SELF-EVALUATION MEMBERS_____

_____

_____

Instructions

When undertaking a self-evaluation the members of the school staff should use the statement of GUIDING PRINCIPLES and CHECKLIST items as an aid to determining the extent to which their school program coincides with the Philosophy and Objectives of the school and meets the needs of the school population and community served. Of necessity a staff will modify statements of Guiding Principles, Checklist items and Evaluations to conform with the philosophy and characteristics of the particular school doing the evaluation. Wherever changes are made the school should explain under Comments the reasons for the change in relation to its own program. Minor differences in terminology should not be regarded as significant items of change.

CHECKLISTS

Checklist items consist of statements deemed applicable to the area of the Criteria being evaluated. These are suggested ideas and are not to be interpreted as the only statements applicable to the area or as all-inclusive. A school may wish to add additional statements of its own that will explain further the particular program of the school. Space is provided in each Checklist for such additions. If the change is regarded as significant, the school will use the letter C in the Checklist as indicated in the following instructions and explain under Comments the precise nature of its offerings.

A staff should note that a definite relation pertains between Checklist items and Evaluations. Members of the staff should familiarize themselves with the definite meanings of Checklist symbols and Evaluation ratings.

CHECKLIST items may be indicated as follows:

E—The statement or condition is *extensive* in application.

M—The statement or condition is *moderately* achieved.

L—The statement or condition is limited in application.

MN—The condition is missing but judged needed by the staff.

N—The condition does not apply to this school.

*C—The condition is achieved in a manner different from Checklist items.

    * Wherever C is used, this aim should be stated in one of the additional numbers of the Checklist and explained under COMMENTS.

EVALUATIONS

Evaluations represent numerical summations of the Checklist items. The rating is determined from discussions of the staff as related to the consistency of the school program with stated Philosophy and Objectives.

To secure a composite view of the school's outcomes in each area of the Criteria, a school will project the Evaluation ratings to the X Blank of the respective areas. A further picture of the total program will be secured by tabulating the Average of the X Blank on the Graphic Summary provided in the Y Blank. Instructions for such procedure are listed in the X and Y Blanks.

Evaluations are indicated as follows:

5—The condition is excellent and extensive. (Please note that 5 does not mean "perfect.")

4—The condition is very good. A school may care to use a further refinement of 4a or 4b: 4a indicates that the condition is extensive and functioning well; 4b indicates that the condition is moderately extensive but functioning excellently.

3—The condition meets student needs to a reasonable degree.

2—The condition is in need of *achievable* improvement.

1—The condition is not being achieved and its need is not recognized.

*MN—The condition is missing but needed.

  *N—The condition does not apply.

    * When MN or N are accepted by the staff for an *Evaluation* rating the divisor on the X Blank must be adjusted accordingly. N should not be used in CHECKLISTS and EVALUATIONS unless the condition absolutely DOES NOT APPLY. If the item is educationally desirable the school should not use N simply because it does not make use of the item. An adequate replacement for the item may fulfill the conditions of the Checklist.

I. Organization

( ) 1. Instruction in art is available to students at every level.

( ) 2. Provision is made for the students to use a variety of art media.

( ) 3. Special classes are arranged for students with particular interests and abilities.

( ) 4. The art program is articulated with the courses of the secondary school.

( ) 5. Provision is made for cooperative planning of work by classroom teachers with an art consultant or art coordinator.

( ) 6. Adequate equipment and facilities are made available for art classes.

( ) 7.

( ) 8.

SUPPLEMENTARY DATA

Grade	Enrollment	No. of Sections	Program or Course of Study	Minutes per Week	No. in Special Classes
K					
1					
2					
3					
4					
5					
6					
7					
8					

EVALUATIONS

( ) a. *How adequate is the instruction in art for all students?*

( ) b. *To what extent is the art program articulated with the art courses of the secondary school?*

( ) c. *To what extent is cooperative planning practiced?*

( ) d. *How adequate are facilities for art instruction?*

COMMENTS

II. Nature of Offerings

CHECKLIST

(   )   1. The program for each grade is so planned as to provide opportunities for sensitive observation, creative expression, experience in manipulation of materials and tools, supplemented by appreciation of our art heritage.

(   )   2. The program provides for sequential instruction according to the age level.

(   )   3. Opportunity is provided for work with: (check)

     _____ cardboard
     _____ chalk
     _____ charcoal
     _____ cord
     _____ crayons
     _____ fibers
     _____ found objects
     _____ ink
     _____ leather
     _____ linoleum
     _____ metal
     _____ paper
     _____ papier mache
     _____ plaster

     _____ plastic
     _____ poster paints
     _____ string
     _____ textiles
     _____ water colors
     _____ wire
     _____ wood
     _____ yarn
     _____ miscellaneous

(   )   4. Stress is placed on freedom of expression and the creative process.

(   )   5. Quality and techniques are emphasized in accordance with the maturity of the student.

(   )   6. Each student does his own work and avoids stereotypes or imitation of others.

(   )   7. Students are given opportunity to discuss and evaluate their own art.

(   )   8. The program provides for art appreciation.

(   )   9.

(   )   10.

EVALUATIONS

(   )   *a. To what extent does the program encourage sensitive observation?*

(   )   *b. To what extent is sequential instruction evident from grade to grade?*

(   )   *c. To what extent is the use of various media encouraged and demonstrated?*

(   )   *d. To what extent does the program favor exploration, discovery, and individual expression?*

(   )   *e. To what extent is student evaluation used as an aid to learning?*

COMMENTS

III. Physical Facilities

(   ) 1. Art is taught in the regular classroom with provision for large or group projects in more spacious locations.

(   ) 2. Water supply is available and adequate.

(   ) 3. Storage space is provided for supplies.

(   ) 4. Storage space for uncompleted work is available.

(   ) 5. Exhibition space is available for display of finished art work and for loan exhibits from out-of-school sources.

(   ) 6. Multi-sensory equipment is available for use of art classes.

(   ) 7.

(   ) 8.

EVALUATIONS

(   ) *a. To what extent is sufficient work space provided?*

(   ) *b. How adequate is the light and water supply?*

(   ) *c. To what extent is storage space provided?*

(   ) *d. How adequate is the multi-sensory equipment?*

COMMENTS

IV. Direction of Learning

A. INSTRUCTIONAL STAFF

CHECKLIST

(   ) 1. Art is taught by the regular classroom teacher assisted by an art consultant or coordinator.

(   ) 2. The art consultant has a college degree with at least a minor in art education, including methods of teaching art in the elementary school.

(   ) 3. The art consultant or coordinator aids the teacher: (check)

    ——— by professional advice on teaching problems.

    ——— in making weekly, monthly and semester plans according to the books or course of study adopted for the community, diocese or locality.

    ——— in evaluating student work and judging student progress.

(   ) 4. The art consultant takes refresher courses, attends art teacher conferences, and keeps abreast of new developments in art education.

(   ) 5. Classroom teachers conducting their own art sessions: (check)

    ——— have preparation in elementary art instruction.

——— take advantage of in-service workshops, demonstrations, television courses, summer school classes, etc.

——— keep their teaching methods up-to-date by frequent recourse to new art books and periodicals, and by personal consultation with successful teachers.

——— avoid stereotyped methods: tracing, hectograph, copying, teacher-dictation, and similar restrictive methods.

——— understand contemporary developments in art and the psychology of children's art expression.

——— arrange exhibits, open-house demonstrations, art fairs, and other activities designed to acquaint faculty, parents, and students with the art activities of the school.

(   ) 6.

(   ) 7.

EVALUATIONS

(   ) *a. How satisfactory is the art preparation of consultants?*

(   ) *b. How adequate is the art preparation of classroom teachers?*

(   ) *c. How extensively does the teaching promote community appreciation in art and allied areas?*

COMMENTS

B. INSTRUCTIONAL ACTIVITIES

CHECKLIST

( ) 1. Motivation is geared toward the special interests and activities of class groups.

( ) 2. Students have a voice in planning and evaluating their art experience.

( ) 3. Art activities are integrated with work in other fields: religion, literature, drama, music, social studies, etc.

( ) 4. Planned field trips are taken to places of art interest.

( ) 5. Instructional activities in primary grades include: (check)

_____ development of sensitivity by self-identification, bodily movements, and observation.

_____ development of skill in using crayons, poster paints, torn and cut paper, clay modeling, cloth, yarn, string collage, and found materials.

_____ developing appreciation of movement, color, dark-light, and rhythm; of beauty in nature, animals, and man-made objects.

( ) 6. Instructional activities in intermediate grades include: (check)

_____ development of sensitivity by observation of natural rhythms, shape, space, volume, texture and color.

_____ development of skill in using a variety of processes and materials, space organization, direct painting, group projects.

_____ development of appreciation of design in nature and art.

( ) 7. Instructional activities in the upper grades include: (check)

_____ development of sensitivity by observation of basic forms, color qualities and changes, qualities of materials, structure, and expressiveness of forms.

_____ development of skill by organized structures in various mediums, planned harmonies of color, shape, textures, and combinations of materials.

( ) 8.

( ) 9.

EVALUATIONS

( ) *a. To what extent are art activities integrated with other subject areas?*

( ) *b. To what extent is there evidence of sequential progress from grade to grade?*

( ) *c. To what extent are the activities structured to develop an appreciation of art?*

COMMENTS

C. INSTRUCTIONAL MATERIALS

CHECKLIST

(   ) 1. The following materials are provided:

     _____ hand tools, such as, saws, drills, hammers, wire cutters, linoleum cutters, brayers, scissors.

     _____ brushes, painting materials, adhesives, paper of various kinds, clay, craft and construction materials, chalk and other materials.

(   ) 2. Provision is made for easily available:

     _____ art prints and reproductions.

_____ art magazines and books at children's proper reading level.

_____ films.

_____ slides.

_____ filmstrips.

_____ exchange exhibitions.

(   ) 3.

(   ) 4.

EVALUATIONS

(   ) *a. How extensive is the variety of materials and tools?*

(   ) *b. To what extent are tools and materials available?*

COMMENTS

D. METHOD OF EVALUATION

CHECKLIST

(   ) 1. Teachers and students collaborate in establishing values for judging art work.

(   ) 2. Teachers and students constructively criticize art products.

(   ) 3. Appraisal is made of art program by authorities in the field.

(   ) 4.

(   ) 5.

EVALUATIONS

(   ) *a. How well do teachers and students evaluate art products?*

(   ) *b. To what extent do authorities participate in evaluating the art program?*

COMMENTS

V. Outcomes

EVALUATIONS

(   ) *a. To what extent is visual awareness heightened by the art program?*
(   ) *b. To what extent is the art work an expression of personal experience?*
(   ) *c. To what degree is there evidence of increased skill in art activities?*
(   ) *d. To what degree are teacher-dictated procedures avoided?*
(   ) *e. To what extent is there evidence of increased appreciation of our art heritage?*
(   ) *f. To what extent does the work of the students measure up to the age level norms?*
(   ) *g. To what extent are libraries, museums, exhibits, and other cultural opportunities used to enrich the program?*

VI. Special Characteristics of Art

1. In what respects is the art program satisfactory and commendable?

    a.

    b.

    c.

    d.

2. In what respects is there greatest need for improving the art program?

    a.

    b.

    c.

    d.

VII. General Evaluation of Instruction in Art

EVALUATIONS

(   ) *a. To what extent is instruction in art consistent with the philosophy and objectives given in Section B?*
(   ) *b. To what extent does instruction in art meet the needs of the students indicated in Section C?*
(   ) *c. To what extent is the school studying problems in the area of art and seeking solutions?*

Formulated and Edited by the Criteria Committee, Elementary School
Department of The National Catholic Educational Association

English Language Arts

GUIDING PRINCIPLES

The English language arts program includes listening, speaking, reading, and writing. Instruction and activities are designed to insure sequential, cumulative, and integrated learning. Attention is given to development of basic skills and to an understanding of form and structure of the language essential to the art of oral and written communication. The program is based upon planned instruction in logical thinking, disciplined listening, clear and effective speaking, intelligent and critical reading, and correct personal and creative writing.

The English language arts program also recognizes and accepts responsibility to contribute to growth in Christian social living through such processes as developing personal responsibility in individual and group activities, inculcating courtesy in discussion, developing correct values in the selection of worthwhile reading materials, and establishing standards of evaluation of mass media. Every effort is made to integrate the language arts with other areas of the curriculum.

The English language arts are basic to the effectiveness of the total elementary program since they prepare students to listen intelligently and to communicate effectively. They broaden and enrich each student's life by developing a sense of personal satisfaction in reading, joy in creative expression and dramatization, and an appreciation of good literature.

NAME OF SCHOOL_____ DATE_____

ADDRESS_____

(ARCH)DIOCESE OF_____

SELF-EVALUATION MEMBERS_____

_____

_____

Instructions

When undertaking a self-evaluation the members of the school staff should use the statement of GUIDING PRINCIPLES and CHECKLIST items as an aid to determining the extent to which their school program coincides with the Philosophy and Objectives of the school and meets the needs of the school population and community served. Of necessity a staff will modify statements of Guiding Principles, Checklist items and Evaluations to conform with the philosophy and characteristics of the particular school doing the evaluation. Wherever changes are made the school should explain under Comments the reasons for the change in relation to its own program. Minor differences in terminology should not be regarded as significant items of change.

CHECKLISTS

Checklist items consist of statements deemed applicable to the area of the Criteria being evaluated. These are suggested ideas and are not to be interpreted as the only statements applicable to the area or as all-inclusive. A school may wish to add additional statements of its own that will explain further the particular program of the school. Space is provided in each Checklist for such additions. If the change is regarded as significant, the school will use the letter C in the Checklist as indicated in the following instructions and explain under Comments the precise nature of its offerings.

A staff should note that a definite relation pertains between Checklist items and Evaluations. Members of the staff should familiarize themselves with the definite meanings of Checklist symbols and Evaluation ratings.

CHECKLIST items may be indicated as follows:

E—The statement or condition is *extensive* in application.

M—The statement or condition is *moderately* achieved.

L—The statement or condition is limited in application.

MN—The condition is missing but judged needed by the staff.

N—The condition does not apply to this school.

*C—The condition is achieved in a manner different from Checklist items.

 * Wherever C is used, this aim should be stated in one of the additional numbers of the Checklist and explained under COMMENTS.

EVALUATIONS

Evaluations represent numerical summations of the Checklist items. The rating is determined from discussions of the staff as related to the consistency of the school program with stated Philosophy and Objectives.

To secure a composite view of the school's outcomes in each area of the Criteria, a school will project the Evaluation ratings to the X Blank of the respective areas. A further picture of the total program will be secured by tabulating the Average of the X Blank on the Graphic Summary provided in the Y Blank. Instructions for such procedure are listed in the X and Y Blanks.

Evaluations are indicated as follows:

5—The condition is excellent and extensive. (Please note that 5 does not mean "perfect.")

4—The condition is very good. A school may care to use a further refinement of 4a or 4b: 4a indicates that the condition is extensive and functioning well; 4b indicates that the condition is moderately extensive but functioning excellently.

3—The condition meets student needs to a reasonable degree.

2—The condition is in need of *achievable* improvement.

1—The condition is not being achieved and its need is not recognized.

*MN—The condition is missing but needed.

 *N—The condition does not apply.

 * When MN or N are accepted by the staff for an *Evaluation* rating the divisor on the X Blank must be adjusted accordingly. N should not be used in CHECKLISTS and EVALUATIONS unless the condition absolutely DOES NOT APPLY. If the item is educationally desirable the school should not use N simply because it does not make use of the item. An adequate replacement for the item may fulfill the conditions of the Checklist.

I. Organization

CHECKLIST

( ) 1. English language arts instruction is required at every level.

( ) 2. The English language arts program is organized to provide for sequential development in the areas of listening, speaking, reading, writing, and in the study of the English language and its literature.

( ) 3. Within each class students are grouped for instruction on the basis of their specific needs.

( ) 4. Flexibility in grouping is an accepted practice.

( ) 5. The basic English language arts program is adapted to meet the needs of the less able students.

( ) 6. Enrichment activities which challenge highly capable students are provided.

( ) 7. In addition to regular classroom instruction, therapeutic activities are provided for students with speech defects.

( ) 8. A program of basic reading skills is provided at all levels.

( ) 9. Corrective and remedial programs are provided for students with reading disabilities.

( ) 10. In departmentalized scheduling the teacher load permits time for attention to students' written work.

( ) 11. Organizational plans consider articulation with the secondary school.

( ) 12.

( ) 13.

SUPPLEMENTARY DATA *(Refer to chart on page 54)*

EVALUATIONS

( ) *a. How adequate are offerings in the English language arts program to meet the needs of all the students?*

( ) *b. How adequate are special provisions to meet the needs of the gifted or remedial students?*

COMMENTS *(Describe any special features of the English language arts program, such as: planning for language as an essential part of all activities in the classroom, integrated teaching of the English language arts, team teaching, special help periods, teacher aides, reading laboratories, individualized reading, use of educational television, etc.)*

SUPPLEMENTARY DATA*

GRADE OR LEVEL	PROGRAM OR COURSE OF STUDY	TEXTS IN USE	ENROLLMENT	NO. OF SECTIONS	RANGE OF CLASS SIZE	MINUTES PER WEEK
K						
1						
2						
3						
4						
5						
6						
7						
8						

* *All areas* of the English language arts program are to be considered.

II. Nature of Offerings

(   ) 1. The English language arts are integrated throughout the elementary school.

(   ) 2. New trends in language arts instruction are evident.

(   ) 3. A knowledge of the history and structure of the English language is developed at appropriate levels.

(   ) 4. Grammatical concepts are taught functionally through organized activities designed to facilitate correct and effective expression.

(   ) 5. Critical thinking is consistently emphasized.

(   ) 6. Gathering, organizing, and presenting ideas are given primary consideration.

(   ) 7. Emphasis is given to the building of speaking, reading, and writing vocabularies.

(   ) 8. Content material from other subject areas is used in writing and speech activities.

Listening and Speaking:

(   ) 9. Good listening habits are developed through carefully organized instruction.

(   ) 10. Listening instruction:
_____ stimulates student awareness of the importance of good listening habits.
_____ recognizes individual student level of listening ability.
_____ provides for continuous, sequential growth in:
_____ informative listening.
_____ appreciative listening.
_____ critical listening.

(   ) 11. The principles of speech and of speaking are consistently and thoroughly taught.

(   ) 12. Correct speech habits are stressed in all oral communication.

(   ) 13. Corrective instruction is provided for individual speech needs.

(   ) 14. Good listening and speaking habits are fostered through student activities, such as: (check)
_____ announcements, directions.
_____ explanations and descriptions.
_____ conversations.
_____ discussions, panels, roundtables.
_____ storytelling.
_____ dramatizations.
_____ oral reading.
_____ choral speaking.
_____ reports.
_____ reviews of mass media.

Reading and Literature:

(   ) 15. A sequential development program in basic reading skills is provided for every student.

(   ) 16. The basic sequential reading program at every level includes:
_____ word-recognition and vocabulary development.
_____ development of comprehension, work-study, and interpretation skills.

(   ) 17. The sequential developmental reading program is based upon the instructional level of achievement of each student.

(   ) 18. Provision is made for instruction in the specific reading skills needed in content subjects.

(   ) 19. Opportunities are provided for students to develop speed in reading comprehension according to their purpose.

(   ) 20. Opportunities are provided for the student to develop a lasting love for reading.

(   ) 21. A variety of supplementary reading materials is available to meet the needs and interests of individual students:
_____ readers
_____ periodicals
_____ trade books
_____ reference books
_____ dictionaries
_____ thesaurus

(   ) 22. Students are taught standards of evaluation to aid them in the selection of reading material.

(   ) 23. Literary selections are chosen for their aesthetic, spiritual, social, and moral values.

(   ) 24. Opportunities are provided to develop the students' appreciation and enjoyment of various types of literature:
_____ myths and legends
_____ fables
_____ folk tales
_____ fairy tales
_____ fiction
_____ biography
_____ poetry

(   ) 25. Recordings, films, and filmstrips are utilized in the teaching of literary types.

(   ) 26. Provision is made to enrich other subject areas through correlation with literature.

(   ) 27. The study of literature is often used to provide a basis for creative writing.

(   ) 28. Students are taught standards of evaluation of mass media.

(   ) 29. Effective use of the school instructional materials center and public library resources is taught.

II. Nature of Offerings—Continued

Writing:

(   ) 30. Emphasis is placed on content and form in all written communication.

(   ) 31. Writing skills are developed through activities such as: (check)

       _____ announcements.

       _____ news items, editorials for school publications.

       _____ notetaking, outlining.

       _____ reports.

       _____ social and business letters.

       _____ reviews.

       _____ plays.

       _____ poems.

       _____ stories.

       _____ narrative, descriptive, expository paragraphs.

(   ) 32. Students are taught to distinguish between formal and informal language and to use it effectively.

(   ) 33. Students are taught correct use of capitalization and punctuation.

(   ) 34. Opportunities are provided for student proofreading and revision of written work.

(   ) 35. The sequential spelling program develops and maintains basic spelling skills and abilities.

(   ) 36. Spelling consciousness with subsequent accuracy in all written work is consistently emphasized.

(   ) 37. The basic handwriting skills, such as letter formation, spacing, legibility, and neatness are developed and maintained.

(   ) 38.

(   ) 39.

EVALUATIONS

(   ) *a. How well does the program provide for the integration of the English language arts?*

(   ) *b. To what degree is the teaching of English language arts influenced by current research findings?*

(   ) *c. To what extent is instruction in critical thinking provided?*

(   ) *d. How effectively are listening skills taught?*

(   ) *e. How extensive is the variety of speech activities?*

(   ) *f. To what extent is a sequential development program in basic reading skills provided for every student?*

(   ) *g. To what extent do reading materials meet the needs and interests of students?*

(   ) *h. To what extent are literary selections chosen on the basis of aesthetic, spiritual, social, and moral values?*

(   ) *i. To what extent are multi-sensory materials utilized in upgrading literary interpretation?*

(   ) *j. How effective is instruction in written communication?*

(   ) *k. To what extent are varied writing activities provided?*

(   ) *l. How adequately are handwriting and spelling skills developed at all grade levels?*

(   ) *m. To what extent are handwriting and spelling skills maintained in all subject areas?*

COMMENTS

III. Physical Facilities

CHECKLIST

( ) 1. Classrooms are furnished with movable desks or chairs.

( ) 2. Classrooms have adequate shelving and storage space.

( ) 3. Filing equipment is available in all classrooms.

( ) 4. Sufficient bulletin board space, flannelboards, and chalkboards are available in each classroom.

( ) 5. A public address system is available for student use when advantageous.

( ) 6. Classrooms permit efficient use of multi-sensory material.

( ) 7. The following types of equipment are available: (check)

_____ record players
_____ movie projector and screen
_____ opaque projector
_____ overhead projector
_____ tape recorder
_____ radio
_____ television set
_____ filmstrip projector
_____ slide projector
_____ microphone
_____ duplicating equipment
_____ typewriter

( ) 8.

( ) 9.

EVALUATIONS

( ) *a. To what degree do physical facilities meet instructional needs of the English language arts program?*

( ) *b. How extensive are storage facilities?*

( ) *c. To what extent is equipment available to all teachers?*

COMMENTS

IV. Direction of Learning

A. INSTRUCTIONAL STAFF

CHECKLIST

Teachers of English language arts:

(   ) 1. are imbued with the Christian philosophy and objectives of education.

(   ) 2. understand the relationship between language arts and personality development.

(   ) 3. possess a wide cultural background.

(   ) 4. have a knowledge of the history, structure, and use of the English language.

(   ) 5. have professional preparation for teaching of reading.

(   ) 6. have special knowledge of children's literature.

(   ) 7. have adequate training in oral and written communication skills and the teaching of these skills on appropriate levels.

(   ) 8. read current professional literature in the English language arts.

(   ) 9. actively participate in language arts in-service programs.

(   ) 10. give evidence of professionalism in speech habits: good articulation, well-modulated tones, correctness, and propriety.

(   ) 11. recognize language problems and needs of youth.

(   ) 12. are cognizant of factors which influence language growth: (check)

     _____ physical and mental aptitude for language

     _____ environment and socioeconomic status of home, school, peer group, and community

     _____ motivation

     _____ mass media of communication

(   ) 13.

(   ) 14.

EVALUATIONS

(   ) a. *How well do teachers understand the language needs of students?*

(   ) b. *To what extent are teachers prepared to meet these needs?*

(   ) c. *To what extent do teachers evidence knowledge of current trends in the English language arts?*

(   ) d. *To what extent do teachers demonstrate ability to teach the English language arts effectively?*

COMMENTS

B. INSTRUCTIONAL ACTIVITIES

CHECKLIST

( ) 1. The objectives of the English language arts program are clearly formulated.

( ) 2. Systematic organization is evident in planning and preparation for instruction.

( ) 3. All staff members cooperate to improve:
_____ listening.
_____ speaking.
_____ reading.
_____ writing.

( ) 4. Students are prepared properly at every level for subsequent learning in the English language arts.

( ) 5. Adaptations in the English language arts instruction reflect current educational thinking.

( ) 6. Adequate instruction and practice in English language arts skills are provided.

( ) 7. A differentiated program provides for varied student needs, interests, and experiences.

( ) 8. There is evidence of student involvement in the planning, conducting, and evaluating of class activities.

( ) 9. Students constructively criticize other students' work as part of instruction and self-improvement.

( ) 10. Students are instructed in the use of the school's instructional materials center according to grade level requirements.

( ) 11. Students are encouraged to make use of local library facilities.

( ) 12. Provision is made for the teaching and practice of study skills at all levels.

( ) 13. Community resources are utilized in language arts instruction.

( ) 14. The tape recorder is utilized as a means of evaluation in the language arts program.

( ) 15. Small group activities which extend classroom experiences in the English language arts are encouraged.

( ) 16.

( ) 17.

EVALUATIONS

( ) a. How adequate is the planning and preparation for instruction in the English language arts program?
( ) b. To what extent is instruction adapted to the needs of individual students?
( ) c. To what extent are materials from the school's instructional materials center used in English language arts instruction?
( ) d. How effective is teaching in the English language arts program?

COMMENTS

C. INSTRUCTIONAL MATERIALS

CHECKLIST

(   ) 1. A variety of instructional materials is accessible: (check)

_____ basal reading texts for different levels
_____ basal reading workbooks
_____ supplementary readers and anthologies
_____ library books for different reading levels and interests
_____ supplementary developmental reading materials
_____ corrective and remedial reading materials
_____ reading laboratory
_____ basic English texts
_____ basic spelling texts
_____ basic handwriting texts
_____ teacher-prepared study guides
_____ periodicals suited to age levels
_____ pamphlets

_____ paperbacks suited to elementary school students
_____ programmed materials
_____ newspapers
_____ dictionaries
_____ diagnostic test materials
_____ radio
_____ television
_____ films
_____ filmstrips
_____ records and tapes
_____ transparencies
_____ maps and charts
_____ diagrams
_____ pictures
_____ models
_____ up-to-date reading lists
_____ others

EVALUATIONS

(   ) *a. How adequate is the variety of instructional materials?*
(   ) *b. How satisfactory is the quality of instructional materials?*
(   ) *c. How adequate is the quantity of instructional materials?*

COMMENTS

D. METHODS OF EVALUATION

CHECKLIST

( ) 1. Evaluating and recording of class and individual achievement are integral parts of the English language arts program.

( ) 2. A number of testing techniques, such as standardized tests, objective, and essay tests are used.

( ) 3. Participation of students in the evaluation of their own progress is encouraged as a learning activity.

( ) 4. The results of evaluation procedures are used to motivate students.

( ) 5. The use of language in functional situations is evaluated through purposeful activities.

( ) 6. Instruction is planned according to the strengths and weaknesses of students.

( ) 7. Test results are used to identify students of varying abilities.

( ) 8. Reading comprehension is checked consistently.

( ) 9. Progress in reading skills and abilities is evaluated periodically.

( ) 10. A cumulative record is kept of each student's progress in the basic reading program.

( ) 11. Group participation in English language arts activities is evaluated.

( ) 12. In evaluating oral and written assignments, emphasis is given to content, organization, and mechanics.

( ) 13. Spelling and handwriting are included in the evaluation of written work.

( ) 14. The elementary English language arts program is articulated with the secondary English program.

( ) 15.

( ) 16.

EVALUATIONS

( ) *a. How satisfactory are the evaluation procedures in the English language arts?*

( ) *b. How well do teachers use evaluation results to improve the effectiveness of their teaching?*

( ) *c. To what extent do evaluation procedures identify the individual needs of all students in the English language arts?*

( ) *d. To what extent is the elementary English language arts program articulated with that of the secondary school?*

COMMENTS

V. Outcomes

Outcomes represent a general over-all summation of items stressed in preceding sections of each area and indicate relative achievement of aims specified in Sections B and C.

EVALUATIONS

(   ) *a. How consistently do students give evidence of desirable listening habits?*

(   ) *b. How consistently do students practice desirable speech habits in the classroom?*

(   ) *c. How consistently are desirable speech habits used in such areas as the corridors, lunchroom, and playground?*

(   ) *d. How satisfactorily do students comprehend reading materials?*

(   ) *e. To what extent, consistent with age level, do students show an understanding and appreciation of literature?*

(   ) *f. To what extent do students give evidence of desirable independent reading habits?*

(   ) *g. To what degree do students manifest creativity in writing?*

(   ) *h. To what extent do students show proficiency in the use of the English language?*

(   ) *i. To what extent do students show proficiency in handwriting?*

(   ) *j. To what extent do students show proficiency in spelling?*

(   ) *k. To what degree are the cultural aspects of the English language arts program discernible to students?*

VI. Special Characteristics of the English Language Arts Program

1. What are the specific strengths of the English language arts program?

    a.

    b.

    c.

2. What are the specific weaknesses of the English language arts program?

    a.

    b.

    c.

3. What studies has the school made in the last three years or is making now to analyze the effectiveness of the English language arts program?

VII. General Evaluation of Instruction in the English Language Arts

EVALUATIONS

(   ) *a. To what extent is instruction in the English language arts consistent with the philosophy, objectives, and functions of the school as specified in Section B?*

(   ) *b. To what extent does instruction in the English language arts meet the needs of students and community as indicated in Section C?*

(   ) *c. To what extent is the school identifying problems and seeking solutions in the areas of listening, speaking, reading, and writing?*

Formulated and Edited by the Criteria Committee, Elementary School
Department of The National Catholic Educational Association

Foreign Languages

GUIDING PRINCIPLES

The role of America in the society of nations has focused attention on the teaching of foreign languages in the elementary school. The aim of the Catholic elementary schools is to offer foreign languages (ancient and modern) as an integral part of the educational formation. The results achieved will be proportionate to the length of the sequential program, the degree of articulation, and the effectiveness of the classroom teaching.

A well-integrated program of study is basic to unified offerings. Since foreign language learning is a cumulative process, it provides for the progressive development of the four basic skills: listening and understanding, speaking, reading, and writing.

An articulated program considers recent developments in the foreign language field. It has clearly defined goals for each level of the long-range program, a unified methodology at all levels, and properly selected materials. Furthermore, articulation is aided by a committee of language teachers working with a coordinator in promoting inter-level meetings.

The success of the program depends upon the proficiency of the teachers. Language teachers are encouraged to maintain or increase their fluency in the foreign language by attending language institutes, workshops, taking language courses, conversing as frequently as possible with native speakers, and using tapes or other recordings in the foreign language.

Correlation with other subjects in the curriculum further develops attitudes, understandings, and appreciations of the culture of the people whose language is studied.

Progress in foreign language learning depends upon the effectiveness of instructional programs together with the sustained interest and application of the students. Evaluation is a continual process used to improve instruction in the foreign language program.

NAME OF SCHOOL_____ DATE_____

ADDRESS_____

(ARCH)DIOCESE OF_____

SELF-EVALUATION MEMBERS_____

_____

_____

Instructions

When undertaking a self-evaluation the members of the school staff should use the statement of GUIDING PRINCIPLES and CHECKLIST items as an aid to determining the extent to which their school program coincides with the Philosophy and Objectives of the school and meets the needs of the school population and community served. Of necessity a staff will modify statements of Guiding Principles, Checklist items and Evaluations to conform with the philosophy and characteristics of the particular school doing the evaluation. Wherever changes are made the school should explain under Comments the reasons for the change in relation to its own program. Minor differences in terminology should not be regarded as significant items of change.

CHECKLISTS

Checklist items consist of statements deemed applicable to the area of the Criteria being evaluated. These are suggested ideas and are not to be interpreted as the only statements applicable to the area or as all-inclusive. A school may wish to add additional statements of its own that will explain further the particular program of the school. Space is provided in each Checklist for such additions. If the change is regarded as significant, the school will use the letter C in the Checklist as indicated in the following instructions and explain under Comments the precise nature of its offerings.

A staff should note that a definite relation pertains between Checklist items and Evaluations. Members of the staff should familiarize themselves with the definite meanings of Checklist symbols and Evaluation ratings.

CHECKLIST items may be indicated as follows:

E—The statement or condition is *extensive* in application.

M—The statement or condition is *moderately* achieved.

L—The statement or condition is limited in application.

MN—The condition is missing but judged needed by the staff.

N—The condition does not apply to this school.

*C—The condition is achieved in a manner different from Checklist items.

   * Wherever C is used, this aim should be stated in one of the additional numbers of the Checklist and explained under COMMENTS.

EVALUATIONS

Evaluations represent numerical summations of the Checklist items. The rating is determined from discussions of the staff as related to the consistency of the school program with stated Philosophy and Objectives.

To secure a composite view of the school's outcomes in each area of the Criteria, a school will project the Evaluation ratings to the X Blank of the respective areas. A further picture of the total program will be secured by tabulating the Average of the X Blank on the Graphic Summary provided in the Y Blank. Instructions for such procedure are listed in the X and Y Blanks.

Evaluations are indicated as follows:

5—The condition is excellent and extensive. (Please note that 5 does not mean "perfect.")

4—The condition is very good. A school may care to use a further refinement of 4a or 4b: 4a indicates that the condition is extensive and functioning well; 4b indicates that the condition is moderately extensive but functioning excellently.

3—The condition meets student needs to a reasonable degree.

2—The condition is in need of *achievable* improvement.

1—The condition is not being achieved and its need is not recognized.

*MN—The condition is missing but needed.

 *N—The condition does not apply.

  * When MN or N are accepted by the staff for an *Evaluation* rating the divisor on the X Blank must be adjusted accordingly. N should not be used in CHECKLISTS and EVALUATIONS unless the condition absolutely DOES NOT APPLY. If the item is educationally desirable the school should not use N simply because it does not make use of the item. An adequate replacement for the item may fulfill the conditions of the Checklist.

I. Organization

(Check A column for ancient languages and M column for modern languages)

CHECKLIST

A   M

1. In deciding the language offerings the following factors are taken into consideration:
( ) ( )   a. interest in foreign language study
( ) ( )   b. availability of competent teachers
( ) ( )   c. cultural background of community
( ) ( )   d. community resources
( ) ( )   e. continuity of subsequent foreign language instruction provided by the secondary school

2. The following sequential program(s) is/are offered:
( ) ( )   a. K to 8
( ) ( )   b. 3 to 8
( ) ( )   c. 7 to 8
( ) ( )   d. – to –
( ) ( )   e. – to –

A   M

( ) ( ) 3. Students are given the opportunity to begin language study at its first level of instruction.

( ) ( ) 4. The age and grade level of each student is given consideration when planning schedules.

( ) ( ) 5. Special provisions are devised for placement at a proper level of instruction when student has prior knowledge of language.

( ) ( ) 6. Articulation with junior and senior high schools is so planned that there is an uninterrupted sequence in any one language.

( ) ( ) 7.

( ) ( ) 8.

SUPPLEMENTARY DATA

Language Offerings	Grade	Level	Number of Sections	Enrollment	Range of Class Size

Special Instructions: If only one category (ancient or modern) is offered, ignore the average of the following evaluations for each item, and fill in only the parentheses opposite the appropriate A or M category.

EVALUATIONS

a. *To what extent are foreign languages available to students?*
b. *To what extent do the foreign language offerings manifest an integrated sequential program?*
c. *To what extent does the school articulate its foreign language program with that of the secondary school attended by its graduates?*

    a   b   c
A ( ) ( ) ( )
M ( ) ( ) ( )

COMMENTS

II. Nature of Offerings

CHECKLIST

A   M

( ) ( )   1. The foreign language program provides for progressive proficiency in the four basic skills:

( ) ( )   a. listening with understanding

( ) ( )   b. fluency in speaking

( ) ( )   c. reading with understanding according to the level of the student

( ) ( )   d. purposeful writing according to the level of the student

( ) ( )   2. Instructional materials are suitable to the age level and individual needs.

( ) ( )   3. Instructional materials assure class participation through individual and/or group activity.

( ) ( )   4. A variety of multi-sensory aids is available to awaken and sustain students' interests.

A   M

( ) ( )   5. Classes are conducted in the foreign language.

( ) ( )   6. The approach used stresses language as an avenue of communication.

( ) ( )   7. Conversation is functional and related to everyday experiences.

( ) ( )   8. Content provides for sequential development.

( ) ( )   9. The program creates an appreciation of the cultures of other nations.

( ) ( ) 10.

( ) ( ) 11.

( ) ( ) 12.

( ) ( ) 13.

EVALUATIONS

( )   a. *How adequately do the offerings meet the foreign language needs of students?*

( )   b. *To what extent does the foreign language program develop basic skills?*

( )   c. *How adequately does the foreign language content provide for sequential development?*

( )   d. *To what extent is an appreciation of the cultures of other nations inculcated?*

     a   b   c   d

A ( ) ( ) ( ) ( )

M ( ) ( ) ( ) ( )

COMMENTS

III. Physical Facilities

CHECKLIST

A M

1. The physical facilities are adequate to meet the instructional interests and needs of students:

( ) ( ) a. chalkboard space is provided

( ) ( ) b. cork, flannel, and/or magnetic boards are provided

( ) ( ) c. display and storage space is provided for charts and pictures as well as other related materials

A M

( ) ( ) 2. Language classrooms are equipped for effective use of multi-sensory aids.

( ) ( ) 3. Classrooms have acoustically treated ceilings and walls.

( ) ( ) 4.

( ) ( ) 5.

( ) ( ) 6.

EVALUATIONS

( ) a. *How adequate are physical facilities to meet the instructional interests and needs of students in foreign language?*

( ) b. *How well are the classrooms adapted to foreign language instruction?*

   a   b

A ( ) ( )

M ( ) ( )

COMMENTS

IV. Direction of Learning

A. INSTRUCTIONAL STAFF

CHECKLIST

A   M

The foreign language teachers:

( ) ( ) 1. are regular classroom teachers.

( ) ( ) 2. are language specialists.

( ) ( ) 3. have a liberal education.

( ) ( ) 4. understand and speak the foreign language.

( ) ( ) 5. have received special training in foreign language methodology.

( ) ( ) 6. are qualified to teach in the elementary school.

( ) ( ) 7. have a knowledge and an understanding of the psychology of the elementary school child.

( ) ( ) 8. use new media of communication effectively to ensure learning.

A   M

( ) ( ) 9. attend language conferences, workshops, institutes, and/or seminars.

( ) ( ) 10. travel and/or study abroad.

( ) ( ) 11. are acquainted with the culture of the foreign country.

( ) ( ) 12. participate in curriculum planning for foreign languages.

( ) ( ) 13. are members of foreign language associations.

( ) ( ) 14. cooperate with the coordinator in the unification of the foreign language program.

( ) ( ) 15.

EVALUATIONS

a. *How adequate is the professional preparation of foreign language teachers?*

b. *To what extent do teachers of foreign language give evidence of professional advancement?*

c. *To what extent do language teachers actively participate in professional organizations?*

d. *To what extent do foreign language teachers cooperate with the coordinator?*

     a   b   c   d

A ( ) ( ) ( ) ( )

M ( ) ( ) ( ) ( )

COMMENTS

B. INSTRUCTIONAL ACTIVITIES

CHECKLIST

A   M

( ) ( ) 1. Both general and specific objectives are formulated for the teaching of foreign languages.

( ) ( ) 2. There is evidence of remote and immediate preparation and thorough planning to obtain these objectives.

( ) ( ) 3. Instructional activities are planned to provide smooth transition from one level of learning to another.

( ) ( ) 4. Variety of methods and techniques are used in instruction.

( ) ( ) 5. Multi-sensory aids are integrated with regular language.

( ) ( ) 6. Flexibility in the program indicates consideration given to student interests and needs.

A   M

( ) ( ) 7. Opportunity is given to the student for directed self-expression.

( ) ( ) 8. Foreign language activities further correlation with other subjects.

( ) ( ) 9. Library resources are utilized for individual and group research.

( ) ( ) 10. Resources of community are utilized in foreign language instruction.

( ) ( ) 11.

( ) ( ) 12.

( ) ( ) 13.

( ) ( ) 14.

( ) ( ) 15.

EVALUATIONS

( ) *a. How effectively are the anticipated goals accomplished?*

( ) *b. How adequate is teacher planning and preparation for instruction?*

( ) *c. How extensive is articulation of the instructional program with the successive levels of language learning?*

( ) *d. How extensive is the integration of multi-sensory materials with regular language work?*

( ) *e. How adequate is the foreign language program of activities to meet the varying needs and interests of the students?*

	a	b	c	d	e
A	( )	( )	( )	( )	( )
M	( )	( )	( )	( )	( )

COMMENTS

C. INSTRUCTIONAL MATERIALS

CHECKLIST

A   M

( ) ( ) 1. Travel posters, postcards, literature, advertisements, calendars, and samples of foreign money

( ) ( ) 2. Flags, maps, globes, and charts

( ) ( ) 3. Magazines in the foreign language

( ) ( ) 4. Books dealing with the country whose language is being studied

( ) ( ) 5. Cue pictures and other illustrations

( ) ( ) 6. Games relating to the country being studied

( ) ( ) 7. Other realia characteristic of the life in the country being studied

A   M

( ) ( ) 8. Tapes and/or recordings

( ) ( ) 9. Record players, radios, tape recorders, projectors, and/or TV sets

( ) ( ) 10. Kinescopes

( ) ( ) 11. Films, filmstrips, and/or slides

( ) ( ) 12. Programmed instruction materials

( ) ( ) 13. Teacher-prepared instructional study guides

( ) ( ) 14.

( ) ( ) 15.

EVALUATIONS

( ) *a. How adequate is the variety of instructional materials?*

( ) *b. How satisfactory is the quality of instructional materials?*

( ) *c. To what extent are the instructional materials available?*

( ) *d. To what extent are the instructional materials utilized?*

( ) *e. To what extent are the instructional materials an integral part of the foreign language program?*

    a   *b*   *c*   *d*   *e*

A ( ) ( ) ( ) ( ) ( )

M ( ) ( ) ( ) ( ) ( )

COMMENTS

D. METHODS OF EVALUATION

CHECKLIST

A   M
( ) ( ) 1. Effectiveness of language instruction is measured in terms of objectives and methods.

( ) ( ) 2. Formal and informal tests are administered in evaluating individual and group progress at each level of instruction.

( ) ( ) 3. Listening comprehension and speaking skills are evaluated on all levels in proportion to the emphasis placed on each skill.

( ) ( ) 4. Reading and writing skills are evaluated at the level of instruction in proportion to the emphasis placed on each skill.

A   M
( ) ( ) 5. Opportunities for self and group evaluation are provided.

( ) ( ) 6. There is continuous checking of intonation and pronunciation by one proficient in the language.

( ) ( ) 7. Follow-up studies of foreign language students are used to identify problem areas and to improve the program.

( ) ( ) 8.

( ) ( ) 9.

( ) ( ) 10.

EVALUATIONS

( ) a. *How extensively do teachers use evaluation to measure teaching effectiveness?*
( ) b. *How extensively do teachers use evaluation to measure pupil achievement?*
( ) c. *How adequate are the instruments of student evaluation?*
( ) d. *To what extent are methods of evaluation used to improve the program?*

    a   b   c   d
A ( ) ( ) ( ) ( )
M ( ) ( ) ( ) ( )

COMMENTS

V. Outcomes

EVALUATIONS

a. *To what extent do students of foreign language exhibit ability to understand the spoken language consistent with age level?*

b. *To what extent do students exhibit the ability to speak the foreign language in functional situations with acceptable intonation and pronunciation?*

c. *To what extent do students on each level read and write the foreign language?*

d. *To what extent do students evidence growth in cultural understanding and appreciation of the people and country whose language is studied?*

	a	b	c	d
A	( )	( )	( )	( )
M	( )	( )	( )	( )

COMMENTS

VI. Special Characteristics of Foreign Language Program

1. In what respects is the foreign language program most satisfactory and commendable?

a.

b.

c.

d.

2. In what respects is there greatest need for improving the foreign language program?

a.

b.

c.

d.

VII. General Evaluation of Instruction in Foreign Language

EVALUATIONS

a. *To what extent is instruction in foreign language consistent with the philosophy and objectives given in Section B?*

b. *To what extent does instruction in foreign language meet the needs of students indicated in Section C?*

c. *To what extent is the school identifying problems in foreign language instruction and seeking their solution?*

	a	b	c
A	( )	( )	( )
M	( )	( )	( )

Formulated and Edited by the Criteria Committee, Elementary School
Department of The National Catholic Educational Association

Geography

GUIDING PRINCIPLES

The geography program at the elementary level consists of instruction and learning activities designed to meet student needs. This subject provides man with a knowledge of God's gifts in nature and an appreciation of the cultural environment of the peoples of the earth. A flexible and sequentially-developed program in geography enables students to integrate the physical and cultural elements of the earth in terms of variations of space and to examine the reasons why these variations exist. This subject reveals the significance of similarities and differences between one environment and another, as geography involves interpretation as well as observation and description.

In addition, the program of geography is designed: 1) to provide students with a true perspective of their relationships with all peoples, emphasizing likenesses rather than differences; 2) to give them an understanding of the interdependence of all nations; 3) to make them aware that a natural element becomes a resource only when man recognizes its usefulness; and 4) to prepare them to become functioning and contributing members of an increasingly complex democratic society.

Provisions are made for students to develop critical thinking and intelligent reflection in the use of geographic materials such as globes, maps, charts, statistical tables, and texts. Skill in the use of these instructional aids helps the students analyze, interpret, evaluate, and form correct judgments.

Articulation exists between the geography program and those allied programs offered at the secondary level.

NAME OF SCHOOL_____ DATE_____

ADDRESS_____

(ARCH)DIOCESE OF_____

SELF-EVALUATION MEMBERS_____

_____

_____

Instructions

When undertaking a self-evaluation the members of the school staff should use the statement of GUIDING PRINCIPLES and CHECKLIST items as an aid to determining the extent to which their school program coincides with the Philosophy and Objectives of the school and meets the needs of the school population and community served. Of necessity a staff will modify statements of Guiding Principles, Checklist items and Evaluations to conform with the philosophy and characteristics of the particular school doing the evaluation. Wherever changes are made the school should explain under Comments the reasons for the change in relation to its own program. Minor differences in terminology should not be regarded as significant items of change.

CHECKLISTS

Checklist items consist of statements deemed applicable to the area of the Criteria being evaluated. These are suggested ideas and are not to be interpreted as the only statements applicable to the area or as all-inclusive. A school may wish to add additional statements of its own that will explain further the particular program of the school. Space is provided in each Checklist for such additions. If the change is regarded as significant, the school will use the letter C in the Checklist as indicated in the following instructions and explain under Comments the precise nature of its offerings.

A staff should note that a definite relation pertains between Checklist items and Evaluations. Members of the staff should familiarize themselves with the definite meanings of Checklist symbols and Evaluation ratings.

CHECKLIST items may be indicated as follows:

E—The statement or condition is *extensive* in application.

M—The statement or condition is *moderately* achieved.

L—The statement or condition is limited in application.

MN—The condition is missing but judged needed by the staff.

N—The condition does not apply to this school.

*C—The condition is achieved in a manner different from Checklist items.

 * Wherever C is used, this aim should be stated in one of the additional numbers of the Checklist and explained under COMMENTS.

EVALUATIONS

Evaluations represent numerical summations of the Checklist items. The rating is determined from discussions of the staff as related to the consistency of the school program with stated Philosophy and Objectives.

To secure a composite view of the school's outcomes in each area of the Criteria, a school will project the Evaluation ratings to the X Blank of the respective areas. A further picture of the total program will be secured by tabulating the Average of the X Blank on the Graphic Summary provided in the Y Blank. Instructions for such procedure are listed in the X and Y Blanks.

Evaluations are indicated as follows:

5—The condition is excellent and extensive. (Please note that 5 does not mean "perfect.")

4—The condition is very good. A school may care to use a further refinement of 4a or 4b: 4a indicates that the condition is extensive and functioning well; 4b indicates that the condition is moderately extensive but functioning excellently.

3—The condition meets student needs to a reasonable degree.

2—The condition is in need of *achievable* improvement.

1—The condition is not being achieved and its need is not recognized.

*MN—The condition is missing but needed.

*N—The condition does not apply.

 * When MN or N are accepted by the staff for an *Evaluation* rating the divisor on the X Blank must be adjusted accordingly. N should not be used in CHECKLISTS and EVALUATIONS unless the condition absolutely DOES NOT APPLY. If the item is educationally desirable the school should not use N simply because it does not make use of the item. An adequate replacement for the item may fulfill the conditions of the Checklist.

I. Organization

( ) 1. Instruction in geography is provided as indicated in the table below.

( ) 2. The geography program is structured on basic concepts suitable for elementary school students.

( ) 3. A sequential development of concepts is provided.

( ) 4. Provision is made to meet individual differences.

( ) 5. An effort is made to reinforce geographic learning through correlation with other subjects.

( ) 6. The program is articulated with allied offerings of secondary schools in the community.

( ) 7. In developing the geography program maximum use is made of available community resources.

( ) 8. Periodically the staff makes systematic evaluation of the geography program in order to make recommendations concerning necessary changes and improvements.

( ) 9.

( ) 10.

SUPPLEMENTARY DATA

GRADE OR LEVEL	NUMBER OF SECTIONS	TOTAL ENROLLMENT	RANGE OF CLASS SIZE	MINUTES PER WEEK	WEEKS PER YEAR	NUMBER OF TEACHERS	TITLE OF TEXT

EVALUATIONS

( ) *a. How balanced is the geography program in scope, sequence, and time allotment?*

( ) *b. How extensive is the provision made for individual needs of students?*

( ) *c. To what extent are community resources used in developing the curriculum?*

( ) *d. To what extent is there periodic evaluation of the geography program?*

( ) *e. How adequate is the provision for correlation with other subjects?*

COMMENTS

II. Nature of Offerings

CHECKLIST

The teaching of geography includes instruction and learning activities designed to:

(   )   1. stress the basic relationship of man to his physical and cultural environment.

(   )   2. challenge the abilities of all students.

(   )   3. develop in students a realization that this is an ever-changing world.

(   )   4. foster respect for people of other cultures, which will lead to a better understanding of their problems.

(   )   5. give students a world-wide frame of reference from which they can form judgments and learn to evaluate critically international, national, and local problems.

(   )   6. help students grasp the economic and cultural interdependence of people and regions.

(   )   7. teach the value and use of human and natural resources.

Instruction in geography stresses the interrelation and interaction of:

(   )   8. man and his natural environment.

(   )   9. man and the cultural features resulting from economic, social, and political processes.

(   ) 10. geography and other subject areas.

(   ) 11. men of various races, cultures, and creeds.

(   ) 12. man's cultural background and his technology in the use of land.

(   ) 13. maps, charts, graphs, texts, and other instructional materials to geographic instruction.

Instruction in geography offers a sequential program in the following skills:

(   ) 14. recognition of relationship between maps and globes.

(   ) 15. interpretation of pictorial diagrams, charts, graphs, and statistical tables.

(   ) 16. interpretation of keys or legends used on maps, as well as shadings, color scales, and symbols.

(   ) 17. facility in the use of scale of miles.

(   ) 18. use of maps to identify the natural and cultural features of the earth.

(   ) 19. interpretation of special maps such as physical, political, product, rainfall, climatic, natural vegetation, population distribution, and also airline, road maps, contour, and overlays.

(   ) 20. ability to make comparisons and inferences.

(   ) 21. locating, gathering, organizing, and interpreting geographic information.

(   ) 22.

(   ) 23.

EVALUATIONS

(   ) *a. To what extent does the geography program help students to understand their physical and cultural environment?*

(   ) *b. To what extent does the study of geography help students to comprehend the economic and cultural interdependence of men of all nations in this ever-changing world?*

(   ) *c. To what extent does the study of geography contribute to a deeper understanding of other curricular offerings?*

(   ) *d. To what extent does the geography program provide for a sequential development of geographic skills?*

(   ) *e. To what degree does the geography program challenge the abilities of all students?*

COMMENTS

III. Physical Facilities

CHECKLIST

( ) 1. Adequate classroom space is provided to facilitate a variety of activities.

( ) 2. Electrical outlets that conform to safety regulations are accessible for the use of multisensory materials.

( ) 3. Sufficient chalk boards, map railings, and cork boards are available.

( ) 4. Movable furniture facilitates group activity.

( ) 5. Adequate shelves, racks, filing cabinets, and storage space are provided.

( ) 6. A library, well provided with appropriate books, magazines, newspapers, pamphlets, and standard reference books is accessible to teachers and students.

( ) 7. Multi-sensory equipment is provided and available.

( ) 8.

( ) 9.

EVALUATIONS

( ) a. *How satisfactory is the space and layout of the classroom used in teaching geography?*

( ) b. *How satisfactory is the storage space?*

( ) c. *How adequate is the equipment essential to the teaching of geography?*

COMMENTS

IV. Direction of Learning

A. INSTRUCTIONAL STAFF

CHECKLIST

The teachers of geography:

( ) 1. have a liberal education.

( ) 2. have specific preparation in the field of geography.

( ) 3. have knowledge of geographic method suitable for the elementary level.

( ) 4. have first-hand information gained through field work and travel.

( ) 5. hold active membership in geographic organizations and societies.

( ) 6. keep abreast of current events through professional reading.

( ) 7. give evidence of utilizing the results of scholarship and research in their daily instruction.

( ) 8. make effective use of community resources.

( ) 9. appreciate the contributions of other cultures.

( ) 10. continue in-service education through formal study or other professional activities.

( ) 11.

( ) 12.

EVALUATIONS

( ) a. *How adequate is the teacher preparation in the field of geography?*

( ) b. *To what extent are the teachers of geography aware of recent developments in this field?*

( ) c. *To what extent do teachers show continued interest in professional growth?*

COMMENTS

B. INSTRUCTIONAL ACTIVITIES

CHECKLIST

( ) 1. Consideration is given to varied student needs, interests, and experiences.

( ) 2. Provision is made for ability grouping.

( ) 3. Careful planning and preparation for instructional activities are evident.

( ) 4. Resources and agencies of the community are used to enrich the program.

( ) 5. Utilization is made of the experiences of foreign students.

( ) 6. Materials of current interest are a vital part of instruction.

( ) 7. Instruction is adapted to new and changing conditions.

( ) 8. Use is made of multi-sensory materials.

( ) 9. Students are encouraged to participate in discussions and to work in committees.

( ) 10. Opportunities for experience in democratic procedures are provided.

( ) 11. Use is made of modern techniques of instruction.

( ) 12. Students are encouraged to develop an interest in worthwhile leisure activities such as reading, lectures, field trips, museum visits, and travel.

( ) 13.

( ) 14.

EVALUATIONS

( ) a. *How adequately do teachers plan instructional activities?*

( ) b. *To what extent are resources and agencies of the community used to enrich the program?*

( ) c. *To what extent is the content adapted to new and changing conditions?*

( ) d. *To what extent do teachers encourage pupil participation through the use of a variety of techniques?*

COMMENTS

C. INSTRUCTIONAL MATERIALS

CHECKLIST

( ) 1. Texts, pamphlets, atlases, magazines, and newspapers are available.

( ) 2. Encyclopedias, source books and other reference materials are provided.

( ) 3. Reading lists based on the reading ability of the students are available for each unit.

( ) 4. Wall maps, globes, charts, compasses, outline maps, graphs, pictures, slides, filmstrips, and films are part of the classroom equipment.

( ) 5. Catalog of available geographic multi-sensory materials is on file.

( ) 6. Catalog of possible field trips in the community is on file.

( ) 7. Lists are provided of free materials available through community resources.

( ) 8. Professional instructional materials for teachers are readily accessible.

( ) 9. Units, study guides, and assignment sheets are prepared to meet the abilities of individual students.

( ) 10.

( ) 11.

EVALUATIONS

( ) a. *How varied are the instructional materials?*

( ) b. *How adequate is the quantity of instructional materials?*

( ) c. *How satisfactory is the quality of the instructional materials?*

( ) d. *To what degree is use made of community resources?*

( ) e. *To what degree do instructional materials meet the needs of individual students?*

COMMENTS

D. METHODS OF EVALUATION

CHECKLIST

( ) 1. Testing is an important part of the teaching-learning process.

( ) 2. Evaluation of geographic activities is based on clear aims and objectives.

( ) 3. Many types of tests are used such as objective, essay, and tests of map skills.

( ) 4. Evaluative procedures to measure geographic learning include observation, teacher-pupil conferences, checklists, and film interpretations.

( ) 5. Improvement in the construction and marking of teacher-made tests is a faculty project.

( ) 6. Test results are interpreted by students and their parents under the guidance of the teacher.

( ) 7. Test results are used by students to evaluate their own progress.

( ) 8. Accurate records are kept of test results.

( ) 9. Competent evaluation reveals strengths and weaknesses to teachers, students, and parents.

( ) 10. Re-teaching or future learning activities are based on the results of evaluation.

( ) 11.

( ) 12.

EVALUATIONS

( ) a. *How effective is the evaluation of the geography program?*

( ) b. *To what extent do teachers use the results of evaluation to analyze the effectiveness of instruction?*

( ) c. *To what extent are evaluation procedures interpreted to parents?*

( ) d. *How effective are testing procedures in making students aware of the nature of their progress?*

( ) e. *How effective is the testing program in identifying students of superior ability in geography?*

COMMENTS

V. Outcomes

(   ) *a. To what degree do offerings in geography emphasize the cultural contributions of all peoples?*

(   ) *b. To what extent does the study of geography enable students to give more intelligent consideration to current problems—community, national, and international?*

(   ) *c. To what extent do students understand the value of human and natural resources and the need for making better use of them?*

(   ) *d. To what extent does geography help students to develop critical thinking?*

(   ) *e. To what extent do students use the tools of geography in correlation with other subjects?*

(   ) *f. To what extent does the study of geography give students an understanding of how the varied problems of the peoples of the world are related to differences in physical and cultural environment?*

(   ) *g. To what extent is instruction in geography consistent with the objectives?*

(   ) *h. To what extent do students possess a comprehension of geographic concepts and patterns rather than a mere accumulation of facts?*

(   ) *i.*

(   ) *j.*

VI. Special Characteristics of Geography Program

1. What aspects of the geography program are most commendable?

   a.

   b.

   c.

   d.

2. What aspects of the geography program need adaptation or improvement?

   a.

   b.

   c.

   d.

3. What improvements are currently being planned?

   a.

   b.

   c.

   d.

VII. General Evaluation of Instruction in Geography

EVALUATIONS

(   ) *a. To what extent is the instruction in geography consistent with the philosophy and objectives given in Section B?*

(   ) *b. To what extent does instruction in geography meet the needs of students indicated in Section C?*

(   ) *c. To what extent is the school identifying problems in geography instruction and seeking their solution?*

Formulated and Edited by the Criteria Committee, Elementary School
Department of The National Catholic Educational Association

Health and Physical Education

GUIDING PRINCIPLES

Health and Physical Education is an integral part of the school curriculum. It consists of a program of instruction activities and experiences designed to meet the health, safety, physical and recreational need of students.

Christian education includes the development of healthful living habits and right attitudes of mental, emotional, physical and moral health.

The program provides participation in games and activities which will lead to the development of strong, well-poised and organically sound bodies.

All instructional experiences in health and physical activities aim to develop concepts, attitudes and practices which place emphasis on wholesome health habits, cooperative play, intelligent following and responsible leadership which are essential to present and future living.

NAME OF SCHOOL_____ DATE_____

ADDRESS_____

(ARCH)DIOCESE OF_____

SELF-EVALUATION MEMBERS_____

_____

_____

Instructions

When undertaking a self-evaluation the members of the school staff should use the statement of GUIDING PRINCIPLES and CHECKLIST items as an aid to determining the extent to which their school program coincides with the Philosophy and Objectives of the school and meets the needs of the school population and community served. Of necessity a staff will modify statements of Guiding Principles, Checklist items and Evaluations to conform with the philosophy and characteristics of the particular school doing the evaluation. Wherever changes are made the school should explain under Comments the reasons for the change in relation to its own program. Minor differences in terminology should not be regarded as significant items of change.

CHECKLISTS

Checklist items consist of statements deemed applicable to the area of the Criteria being evaluated. These are suggested ideas and are not to be interpreted as the only statements applicable to the area or as all-inclusive. A school may wish to add additional statements of its own that will explain further the particular program of the school. Space is provided in each Checklist for such additions. If the change is regarded as significant, the school will use the letter C in the Checklist as indicated in the following instructions and explain under Comments the precise nature of its offerings.

A staff should note that a definite relation pertains between Checklist items and Evaluations. Members of the staff should familiarize themselves with the definite meanings of Checklist symbols and Evaluation ratings.

CHECKLIST items may be indicated as follows:

E—The statement or condition is *extensive* in application.

M—The statement or condition is *moderately* achieved.

L—The statement or condition is *limited* in application.

MN—The condition is missing but judged needed by the staff.

N—The condition does not apply to this school.

*C—The condition is achieved in a manner different from Checklist items.

 * Wherever C is used, this aim should be stated in one of the additional numbers of the Checklist and explained under COMMENTS.

EVALUATIONS

Evaluations represent numerical summations of the Checklist items. The rating is determined from discussions of the staff as related to the consistency of the school program with stated Philosophy and Objectives.

To secure a composite view of the school's outcomes in each area of the Criteria, a school will project the Evaluation ratings to the X Blank of the respective areas. A further picture of the total program will be secured by tabulating the Average of the X Blank on the Graphic Summary provided in the Y Blank. Instructions for such procedure are listed in the X and Y Blanks.

Evaluations are indicated as follows:

5—The condition is excellent and extensive. (Please note that 5 does not mean "perfect.")

4—The condition is very good. A school may care to use a further refinement of 4a or 4b: 4a indicates that the condition is extensive and functioning well; 4b indicates that the condition is moderately extensive but functioning excellently.

3—The condition meets student needs to a reasonable degree.

2—The condition is in need of *achievable* improvement.

1—The condition is not being achieved and its need is not recognized.

*MN—The condition is missing but needed.

 *N—The condition does not apply.

 * When MN or N are accepted by the staff for an *Evaluation* rating the divisor on the X Blank must be adjusted accordingly. N should not be used in CHECKLISTS and EVALUATIONS unless the condition absolutely DOES NOT APPLY. If the item is educationally desirable the school should not use N simply because it does not make use of the item. An adequate replacement for the item may fulfill the conditions of the Checklist.

I. Organization

CHECKLIST

( ) 1. A planned program in health education is provided.

( ) 2. Health education programs are planned cooperatively by staff members.

( ) 3. Health services are provided by community agencies.

( ) 4. All students are required to take physical education except those excused by a physician.

( ) 5. Physical education classes meet _____ periods each week.

( ) 6. Physical education periods are _____ minutes in length.

( ) 7. Grade level and needs of students are considered.

( ) 8. The program is under the direction of a person trained in physical education.

( ) 9. Provisions are made for students who lack skill in physical education to receive special instruction.

( ) 10. Class size is based upon the personnel, facilities and nature of activities.

( ) 11. Sufficient funds are provided for the physical education program.

( ) 12. Parents are kept informed of the purpose of the physical education program.

( ) 13. Proper protective equipment is provided for all students engaged in sports and activities.

( ) 14. Students are required to have medical examinations before participating in strenuous sports.

( ) 15. Medical assistance is available in case of injury.

( ) 16. Intramural activities are planned, organized and supervised.

( ) 17. Program complies with state laws.

( ) 18. Provision is made for insurance of students.

( ) 19.

( ) 20.

EVALUATIONS

( ) a. *How adequate is the provision for health instruction for all students?*

( ) b. *How satisfactory are time allotments for health education?*

( ) c. *How adequate is the provision for physical education activities?*

( ) d. *How adequate are time allotments for the physical education program?*

( ) e. *How satisfactory are the controls and safeguards for the physical education program?*

II. Nature of Offerings

CHECKLIST

(   ) 1. Stress is placed upon the development of positive attitudes toward safe and healthful living.

(   ) 2. Opportunities are provided for an understanding of the personal and environmental factors affecting health.

(   ) 3. Students are taught the causes and preventions of disease.

(   ) 4. The student's responsibilities both for his own health and for the health of others are stressed.

(   ) 5. Opportunities are provided for the study of safety in the home, school, and community.

(   ) 6. Opportunities are given for each student to acquire understanding of the growth, structure, and function of his own body.

(   ) 7. Provision is made for the study of nutritional needs.

(   ) 8. Opportunities are given students to plan and participate in a balanced program of work, play and rest.

(   ) 9. Opportunities are offered to study the factors affecting mental and emotional health.

(   ) 10. Instruction in First Aid is given students.

(   ) 11. Planned articulation is carried on with high schools in health and physical education.

(   ) 12. Activities are provided for a physical fitness program.

(   ) 13. Activities are provided to meet individual needs, interests, and abilities of students.

(   ) 14. Provisions are made for rhythmic activities.

(   ) 15. Opportunities are provided to develop leadership in physical education.

(   ) 16. Opportunities are provided to participate in group planning.

(   ) 17.

(   ) 18.

EVALUATIONS

(   ) a. *How adequate is the variety of offerings in health education?*

(   ) b. *How adequate is the quality of offerings in health education?*

(   ) c. *How adequate is the content of offerings in developing knowledge, understanding and skill?*

(   ) d. *How adequate is the variety of experiences in physical education?*

(   ) e. *How adequate is the content of experiences in physical education?*

(   ) f. *How adequately does the program provide for leisure-time?*

COMMENTS

III. Physical Facilities

CHECKLIST

( ) 1. Indoor space and facilities are sufficient to accommodate existing class sizes.

( ) 2. Furniture and equipment can be arranged for individual, group work and demonstrations.

( ) 3. Multi-sensory equipment is available.

( ) 4. Opportunity is provided for use of multi-sensory materials.

( ) 5. Ample space is provided for library, reference materials, models, _____

_____

_____

( ) 6. Proper entrance and exit facilities for all physical education areas are arranged.

( ) 7. The play area is sufficient for outdoor activities.

( ) 8. The physical education area is provided with:
_____ first-aid equipment and supplies.
_____ apparatus for muscle development.

_____ rhythmic development materials.
_____ piano.
_____ record player and records.
_____ amplifiers.

( ) 9. The outdoor play area is:
_____ easily reached.
_____ suitably surfaced, graded and drained.
_____ enclosed.
_____ free from safety hazards.
_____ suitable for a variety of activities.
_____ marked for numerous activities.
_____ adequately equipped for activities.

( ) 10.

( ) 11.

EVALUATIONS

( ) a. *How adequate is the equipment for health instruction?*

( ) b. *How adequate are storage facilities for equipment and materials?*

( ) c. *How adequate are provisions for health and safety?*

( ) d. *How adequate are the space and facilities provided for indoor physical education?*

( ) e. *How adequate are the space and facilities for outdoor physical education?*

COMMENTS

IV. Direction of Learning

A. INSTRUCTIONAL STAFF

CHECKLIST

Staff members who have responsibility for organized programs in health and physical education:

(   )   1. have a liberal education.

(   )   2. have had professional preparation in health and physical education.

(   )   3. know current developments in health, safety and physical education.

(   )   4. are thoroughly acquainted with the health and safety programs. (See Section H.)

(   )   5. coordinate the instructional program with community health and safety services.

(   )   6. continue active participation in in-service education.

(   )   7. have knowledge of child growth and development.

(   )   8. dress suitably for physical education instruction.

(   )   9.

(   )   10.

EVALUATIONS

(   )   *a. How adequate is the liberal education background of the staff?*

(   )   *b. How adequate is the staff's preparation in professional health courses for carrying out the health program of the school?*

(   )   *c. How adequate is the preparation of the staff for teaching physical education?*

(   )   *d. To what extent are community health and safety services utilized?*

COMMENTS

B. INSTRUCTIONAL ACTIVITIES

CHECKLIST

( ) 1. Careful planning and preparation precedes instruction.
( ) 2. Teaching is adapted to changing conditions.
( ) 3. Learning activities are planned according to individual needs.
( ) 4. Teaching is centered on health problems of daily living.
( ) 5. Multi-sensory teaching materials and methods are employed.
( ) 6. Physicians, nurses, dentists, policemen, firemen and other resource people are used to supplement instruction.
( ) 7. Teaching is coordinated with the health service program of the school.
( ) 8. Related subjects are coordinated with physical education activities.
( ) 9. Students are encouraged to read current articles on health, safety and physical education.
( ) 10. Community resources are used to enrich instruction.
( ) 11. Individual and group projects are used.

( ) 12. Instructional activities are sequentially planned.
( ) 13. Physical education is correlated with health instruction.
( ) 14. Teaching is directed toward clearly defined objectives in physical education.
( ) 15. Leadership abilities are developed through such activities as:

_____
_____
_____
_____
_____

( ) 16. Students are given opportunities to cooperate with recognized leaders.
( ) 17. Students are given opportunities to assist in planning, conducting and evaluating activities.
( ) 18.
( ) 19.

EVALUATIONS

( ) *a. How adequately is instruction planned to meet the needs of students?*
( ) *b. To what extent is instruction centered on health problems of daily living?*
( ) *c. To what degree are activities conducted with regard for student's health and safety?*
( ) *d. How effective is the teaching in health education?*
( ) *e. How effective is the teaching in physical education?*
( ) *f. To what extent is leadership developed through health and physical education activities?*

COMMENTS

C. INSTRUCTIONAL MATERIALS

CHECKLIST

(   ) 1. Health textbooks and study materials adapted to the reading levels of the student are available.

(   ) 2. Curriculum guides, study guides and resource units are used.

(   ) 3. Sufficient reference material is available.

(   ) 4. Current periodicals pertaining to health, safety, and physical education are used.

(   ) 5. Multi-sensory materials are available, such as:

_____ charts.

_____ record players.

_____

_____

_____

(   ) 6. Commercial sources are utilized in obtaining suitable teaching materials.

(   ) 7. Splints, bandages and first-aid materials are available.

(   ) 8. Official rules books for a variety of sports are available.

(   ) 9. Equipment is provided for a variety of individual and small group activities.

(   ) 10. Necessary equipment for testing is available.

(   ) 11.

(   ) 12.

EVALUATIONS

(   ) a. *How adequate is the variety of instructional materials and equipment?*

(   ) b. *How adequate is the quality of instructional materials and equipment?*

(   ) c. *How adequate is the quantity of instructional materials and equipment?*

(   ) d. *How adequate are the reading and reference materials?*

(   ) e. *To what extent are materials and equipment used by teachers?*

COMMENTS

D. METHODS OF EVALUATION

CHECKLIST

(   ) 1. Evaluation is an integral part of instruction.

(   ) 2. A variety of testing techniques is used.

(   ) 3. Test results are interpreted in planning instruction.

(   ) 4. Effectiveness of instruction is evaluated on the basis of health habits and practices.

(   ) 5. The cooperation of parents is enlisted in the health, safety, and physical education programs.

(   ) 6. Students engage in self-evaluation activities.

(   ) 7. Health and physical education data are appraised in considering the effectiveness of instruction.

(   ) 8. Aptitudes and abilities are considered.

(   ) 9. Height and weight are recorded and studied at specified times.

(   ) 10. Records are kept, relevant to the mental, physical, emotional, and social development of students.

(   ) 11. Standardized and teacher-made tests are used in evaluating physical fitness, knowledge, and skills.

(   ) 12.

(   ) 13.

EVALUATIONS

(   ) a. *To what extent do teachers use methods of evaluation in analyzing the effectiveness of instruction?*

(   ) b. *How comprehensive are evaluation procedures in health education?*

(   ) c. *How comprehensive are evaluation procedures in physical education?*

COMMENTS

V. Outcomes

(No checklist items are prepared for this division, since they would be largely repetitious of the checklist items in preceding divisions.)

EVALUATIONS

( ) *a. To what extent do students demonstrate an understanding of personal health problems?*

( ) *b. To what degree do students show an understanding of community health problems?*

( ) *c. To what degree does the behavior of students give evidence of desirable habits and attitudes related to health, safety, and physical education?*

( ) *d. How satisfactory is the status of health and safety in the school? (Evidence from environmental health and safety studies, cumulative studies of attendance, health appraisal results, and accidents.)*

( ) *e. To what extent have students developed physically strong, healthy, well-coordinated bodies?*

( ) *f. To what degree have students developed knowledge and skill of physical education activities?*

( ) *g. To what degree have students acquired desirable habits of cleanliness and good grooming?*

( ) *h. How adequate are conditions of health and safety in the school?*

( ) *i. To what degree do students show leadership qualities through physical education activities?*

VI. Special Characteristics of Health and Physical Education

1. In what respects is health education most satisfactory and commendable in carrying out the functions of the elementary school?

    a.

    b.

    c.

    d.

2. In what respects is there greatest need for improving health education?

    a.

    b.

    c.

    d.

VI. Special Characteristics of Health and Physical Education, (cont'd.)

3. In what respects is instruction in physical education most satisfactory and commendable in carrying out the functions of the school?

a.

b.

c.

d.

4. In what respects is there greatest need for improving physical education for students?

a.

b.

c.

d.

VII. General Evaluation of Health and Physical Education

EVALUATIONS

(   ) *a. To what extent is instruction in health and physical education consistent with the philosophy and objectives given in Section B?*

(   ) *b. To what extent does instruction in health and physical education meet the needs of students indicated in Section C?*

(   ) *c. To what extent is the school identifying problems in health education and seeking their solution?*

(   ) *d. To what extent is the school identifying problems in physical education and seeking their solution?*

Formulated and Edited by the Criteria Committee, Elementary School
Department of The National Catholic Educational Association

History

GUIDING PRINCIPLES

The course of study in history provides students with information about their heritage so that they may become intelligent citizens of society. History attempts to make the past intelligible in order that the present may be understood and that the future may be more adequately met by men of responsibility.

History courses are designed:

1. to transmit the abiding ethical and cultural heritage of the past;

2. to provide a true historical record of our nation and the world;

3. to inculcate the idea of the dignity of man and the ideal in our free society that people of all races and creeds have equal opportunities;

4. to instill an awareness of obligations toward peoples of all nations;

5. to prepare students for effective American citizenship.

The history classroom serves as a laboratory in which students and teachers explore and practice the principles and ideals of Christian social living. Here is developed a balanced emphasis on the individual and the common good and on the rights and duties of citizenship in a democracy, derived from the principles expressed in basic American documents.

A comprehensive course of study in history utilizes and correlates other areas of the curriculum.

NAME OF SCHOOL_____ DATE_____

ADDRESS_____

(ARCH)DIOCESE OF_____

SELF-EVALUATION MEMBERS_____

_____

_____

Instructions

When undertaking a self-evaluation the members of the school staff should use the statement of GUIDING PRINCIPLES and CHECKLIST items as an aid to determining the extent to which their school program coincides with the Philosophy and Objectives of the school and meets the needs of the school population and community served. Of necessity a staff will modify statements of Guiding Principles, Checklist items and Evaluations to conform with the philosophy and characteristics of the particular school doing the evaluation. Wherever changes are made the school should explain under Comments the reasons for the change in relation to its own program. Minor differences in terminology should not be regarded as significant items of change.

CHECKLISTS

Checklist items consist of statements deemed applicable to the area of the Criteria being evaluated. These are suggested ideas and are not to be interpreted as the only statements applicable to the area or as all-inclusive. A school may wish to add additional statements of its own that will explain further the particular program of the school. Space is provided in each Checklist for such additions. If the change is regarded as significant, the school will use the letter C in the Checklist as indicated in the following instructions and explain under Comments the precise nature of its offerings.

A staff should note that a definite relation pertains between Checklist items and Evaluations. Members of the staff should familiarize themselves with the definite meanings of Checklist symbols and Evaluation ratings.

CHECKLIST items may be indicated as follows:

E—The statement or condition is *extensive* in application.

M—The statement or condition is *moderately* achieved.

L—The statement or condition is limited in application.

MN—The condition is missing but judged needed by the staff.

N—The condition does not apply to this school.

*C—The condition is achieved in a manner different from Checklist items.

   * Wherever C is used, this aim should be stated in one of the additional numbers of the Checklist and explained under COMMENTS.

EVALUATIONS

Evaluations represent numerical summations of the Checklist items. The rating is determined from discussions of the staff as related to the consistency of the school program with stated Philosophy and Objectives.

To secure a composite view of the school's outcomes in each area of the Criteria, a school will project the Evaluation ratings to the X Blank of the respective areas. A further picture of the total program will be secured by tabulating the Average of the X Blank on the Graphic Summary provided in the Y Blank. Instructions for such procedure are listed in the X and Y Blanks.

Evaluations are indicated as follows:

5—The condition is excellent and extensive. (Please note that 5 does not mean "perfect.")

4—The condition is very good. A school may care to use a further refinement of 4a or 4b: 4a indicates that the condition is extensive and functioning well; 4b indicates that the condition is moderately extensive but functioning excellently.

3—The condition meets student needs to a reasonable degree.

2—The condition is in need of *achievable* improvement.

1—The condition is not being achieved and its need is not recognized.

*MN—The condition is missing but needed.

*N—The condition does not apply.

   * When MN or N are accepted by the staff for an *Evaluation* rating the divisor on the X Blank must be adjusted accordingly. N should not be used in CHECKLISTS and EVALUATIONS unless the condition absolutely DOES NOT APPLY. If the item is educationally desirable the school should not use N simply because it does not make use of the item. An adequate replacement for the item may fulfill the conditions of the Checklist.

I. Organization

( ) 1. History courses are taught in grades as indicated in the table below.

( ) 2. Sequential development is provided for in the course of study or manual.

( ) 3. Provision is made to meet individual differences.

( ) 4. Courses in history are planned to provide coordination with instructional activities of other curriculum areas.

( ) 5. Community groups and agencies are consulted in the development of the history program.

( ) 6. The program is articulated with secondary schools in the community.

( ) 7. Periodic evaluation of the courses by teachers or committees is provided.

( ) 8. Provision is made to supplement material.

( ) 9.

( ) 10.

SUPPLEMENTARY DATA

GRADE	NUMBER OF SECTIONS	ENROLLMENT PER CLASS	MINUTES PER WEEK	NUMBER OF TEACHERS	TEXT

EVALUATIONS

( ) a. *To what extent are history courses planned to provide for sequential development?*

( ) b. *How adequate is provision for correlation of the history program with other subjects?*

( ) c. *How adequately is provision made for supplementation?*

( ) d. *To what extent do time allotments satisfactorily meet instructional needs?*

COMMENTS

II. Nature of Offerings

CHECKLIST

(   )   1. The content of the history program is designed to transmit the spiritual and cultural heritage of the past.

(   )   2. A true comprehensive historical record of our nation and of the world is stressed.

(   )   3. Current topics, problems and issues, both national and international, are an integral part of the history program.

(   )   4. The abilities of all students are challenged.

(   )   5. Responsibility for democratic action in the conduct of school activities is encouraged.

(   )   6. Efforts are made to help students recognize and deal with propaganda.

(   )   7. Christian social consciousness is developed.

(   )   8. Responsibilities and duties as well as rights of individuals in a democracy are emphasized.

(   )   9. A wholesome allegiance to the ideals of American democracy is developed.

(   ) 10. The mind of the Church, as reflected in the social encyclicals, is explained, studied, and discussed.

(   ) 11.

(   ) 12.

EVALUATIONS

(   )   *a. To what extent are religious, social, political, and economic issues included in the history program?*

(   )   *b. To what extent do the history courses encourage students to evaluate their own beliefs, attitudes, values, and social conduct?*

(   )   *c. To what extent do the history courses challenge the abilities of all the students?*

(   )   *d. To what extent do the history courses strengthen allegiance to the American way of life based on Christian principles?*

COMMENTS

III. Physical Facilities

( ) 1. Classroom facilities are arranged to provide for a variety of activities.

( ) 2. Bookshelves, display areas, map rails, and filing cabinets are provided and are readily accessible in each room.

( ) 3. Classrooms are properly equipped for the effective use of multi-sensory aids.

( ) 4. Multi-sensory equipment is available and accessible.

( ) 5.

( ) 6.

( ) 7.

( ) *a. How adequate is the space for instructional activities?*

( ) *b. How adequate are provisions for the use of multi-sensory materials?*

IV. Direction of Learning

A. INSTRUCTIONAL STAFF

CHECKLIST

The teachers of history:

(   ) 1. have a liberal education.
(   ) 2. have adequate background in history.
(   ) 3. have professional education background.
(   ) 4. have an awareness of contemporary affairs.
(   ) 5. participate as members of committees involved in the preparation of curriculum, selection of textbooks and other instructional materials.

(   ) 6. continue other in-service education.
(   ) 7. participate in community activities and public affairs.

(   ) 8.

(   ) 9.

EVALUATIONS

(   ) *a. How adequate is the preparation of teachers of history?*
(   ) *b. To what extent do teachers of history give evidence of knowledge of contemporary affairs?*
(   ) *c. To what extent do teachers of history show continued interest in professional growth?*

COMMENTS

B. INSTRUCTIONAL ACTIVITIES

CHECKLIST

(   ) 1. Instructional activities are carefully planned.
(   ) 2. Specific objectives in the history program provide for good citizenship.
(   ) 3. The varying abilities of students are considered in planning.
(   ) 4. Techniques such as reports, discussions, and forums are used.
(   ) 5. Experiences in democratic procedures are provided in the classroom.

(   ) 6. The resources of the community are used to enrich learning activities.
(   ) 7. The history program is integrated with other curriculum areas.
(   ) 8. Current event materials are used.

(   ) 9.

(   ) 10.

EVALUATIONS

(   ) *a. How adequately do history teachers plan instructional activities?*
(   ) *b. To what extent do teachers use appropriate teaching procedures?*
(   ) *c. To what extent are contemporary affairs related to instruction?*

COMMENTS

C. INSTRUCTIONAL MATERIALS

CHECKLIST

( ) 1. Materials suited to students' reading levels are available.

( ) 2. An adequate supply of multi-sensory equipment and materials is accessible.

( ) 3. Maps, charts, models, globes, filmstrips and similar instructional materials are readily available.

( ) 4. Appropriate study guides are available to all students.

( ) 5. A variety of resource unit materials is available for the use of the teacher.

( ) 6. Student reference materials stressing significant aspects of the history program are available.

( ) 7.

( ) 8.

EVALUATIONS

( ) *a. How adequate is the variety of instructional materials?*

( ) *b. How adequate is the quality of instructional materials?*

COMMENTS

D. METHOD OF EVALUATION

CHECKLIST

( ) 1. Evaluation activities are considered an integral part of the teaching-learning process.

( ) 2. Methods of evaluation are appropriate to the objectives desired.

( ) 3. Varied tests are used, including standardized tests and teacher-made objective and essay tests.

( ) 4. Unified efforts are made to improve construction and grading of teacher-made tests.

( ) 5. Students participate in the evaluation of their own progress.

( ) 6. Systematic records are kept of the results of evaluations.

( ) 7. Evaluation results are used to plan subsequent learning activities.

EVALUATIONS

( ) *a. How comprehensive are the evaluation procedures in the history program?*

( ) *b. How well do teachers use the results of evaluation procedures in analyzing the effectiveness of their teaching?*

( ) *c. How well do evaluation procedures help students understand the nature of their progress?*

( ) *d. To what extent are evaluation procedures used to identify students of unusual promise in the field of history?*

COMMENTS

V. Outcomes

(No checklist items are prepared for this division since they would be largely repetitions of checklist items in preceding divisions.)

EVALUATIONS

(   ) *a. To what degree do students exhibit understanding and appreciation of their historical heritage?*

(   ) *b. To what degree do students exhibit an understanding of the growth and development of American institutions?*

(   ) *c. To what degree do students exhibit an understanding of current local, national, and international issues and problems?*

(   ) *d. To what degree do students exhibit a knowledge of place and time necessary to an understanding of local, national and world affairs?*

(   ) *e. To what degree do students exhibit the ability to examine critically their beliefs, attitudes, values, and social conduct based on Christian principles?*

(   ) *f. To what degree do students exhibit an understanding of individual rights and responsibilities?*

(   ) *g. To what degree do students successfully assume and discharge civic responsibility in school?*

(   ) *h. To what degree do students successfully assume and discharge civic responsibility in the community?*

VI. Special Characteristics of History as Taught in this School

1. The history program in this school is commendable in the following:

a.

b.

c.

2. The history instruction in this school can be improved in the following:

a.

b.

c.

VII. General Evaluation of Instruction in History

EVALUATIONS

(   ) *a. To what extent is instruction in history consistent with the philosophy and objectives given in Section B?*

(   ) *b. To what extent does instruction in history meet the needs of students indicated in Section C?*

(   ) *c. To what extent is the school identifying problems in history instruction and seeking their solution?*

Formulated and Edited by the Criteria Committee, Elementary School
Department of The National Catholic Educational Association

Mathematics

GUIDING PRINCIPLES

The elementary school mathematics program consists of a sequential development of instruction and activities designed to contribute to the common and individual needs of students in grades K-8.

Designed to foster an attitude of inquiry in elementary school students, the program utilizes the discovery method of learning. Emphasis is placed upon the important unifying concepts of mathematics. Its linear structure is based upon psychological principles of motivation, readiness, ability levels, and maturity.

The program is aimed at developing the ability (1) to understand the basic concepts, patterns, and relationships which reveal the structure of mathematics; (2) to develop a knowledge and use of the precise terminology of mathematics; (3) to recognize the basic structure of problem situations, to acquire facility in their solution, and to formulate new problems; (4) to acquire accuracy, precision and skill in computation, as well as an understanding of the principles governing the fundamental operations.

Ultimately the mathematics program is intended to give students the mathematical competence needed to function in a technical and complex society, and to foster in capable students an interest in mathematics or science as a future career.

NAME OF SCHOOL_____ DATE_____

ADDRESS_____

(ARCH)DIOCESE OF_____

SELF-EVALUATION MEMBERS_____

_____

_____

Instructions

When undertaking a self-evaluation the members of the school staff should use the statement of GUIDING PRINCIPLES and CHECKLIST items as an aid to determining the extent to which their school program coincides with the Philosophy and Objectives of the school and meets the needs of the school population and community served. Of necessity a staff will modify statements of Guiding Principles, Checklist items and Evaluations to conform with the philosophy and characteristics of the particular school doing the evaluation. Wherever changes are made the school should explain under Comments the reasons for the change in relation to its own program. Minor differences in terminology should not be regarded as significant items of change.

CHECKLISTS

Checklist items consist of statements deemed applicable to the area of the Criteria being evaluated. These are suggested ideas and are not to be interpreted as the only statements applicable to the area or as all-inclusive. A school may wish to add additional statements of its own that will explain further the particular program of the school. Space is provided in each Checklist for such additions. If the change is regarded as significant, the school will use the letter C in the Checklist as indicated in the following instructions and explain under Comments the precise nature of its offerings.

A staff should note that a definite relation pertains between Checklist items and Evaluations. Members of the staff should familiarize themselves with the definite meanings of Checklist symbols and Evaluation ratings.

CHECKLIST items may be indicated as follows:

E—The statement or condition is *extensive* in application.

M—The statement or condition is *moderately* achieved.

L—The statement or condition is limited in application.

MN—The condition is missing but judged needed by the staff.

N—The condition does not apply to this school.

*C—The condition is achieved in a manner different from Checklist items.

* Wherever C is used, this aim should be stated in one of the additional numbers of the Checklist and explained under COMMENTS.

EVALUATIONS

Evaluations represent numerical summations of the Checklist items. The rating is determined from discussions of the staff as related to the consistency of the school program with stated Philosophy and Objectives.

To secure a composite view of the school's outcomes in each area of the Criteria, a school will project the Evaluation ratings to the X Blank of the respective areas. A further picture of the total program will be secured by tabulating the Average of the X Blank on the Graphic Summary provided in the Y Blank. Instructions for such procedure are listed in the X and Y Blanks.

Evaluations are indicated as follows:

5—The condition is excellent and extensive. (Please note that 5 does not mean "perfect.")

4—The condition is very good. A school may care to use a further refinement of 4a or 4b: 4a indicates that the condition is extensive and functioning well; 4b indicates that the condition is moderately extensive but functioning excellently.

3—The condition meets student needs to a reasonable degree.

2—The condition is in need of *achievable* improvement.

1—The condition is not being achieved and its need is not recognized.

*MN—The condition is missing but needed.

*N—The condition does not apply.

* When MN or N are accepted by the staff for an *Evaluation* rating the divisor on the X Blank must be adjusted accordingly. N should not be used in CHECKLISTS and EVALUATIONS unless the condition absolutely DOES NOT APPLY. If the item is educationally desirable the school should not use N simply because it does not make use of the item. An adequate replacement for the item may fulfill the conditions of the Checklist.

I. Organization

CHECKLIST

( ) 1. The study of mathematics is required at every level of the elementary school.

( ) 2. Sequence and articulation are in evidence between the various levels of the school.

( ) 3. A contemporary program of mathematics is provided for all students.

( ) 4. Non-graded organization is in operation.

( ) 5. Ability grouping or provision for small group instruction within the larger group is used.

( ) 6. A special program of learning for gifted students is offered.

( ) 7. A special program of remedial instruction is offered.

( ) 8. Mathematics is correlated with other subject areas.

( ) 9. Departmentalization exists in the upper grades.

( ) 10. Departmentalization exists in the intermediate grades.

( ) 11. Team teaching is employed.

( ) 12. Televised teaching is utilized.

( ) 13. The mathematics program is properly articulated with the programs of other elementary schools and of secondary schools within the area.

( ) 14. A mathematics coordinator within the school or from an outside agency assumes responsibility for the organization of the mathematics program.

( ) 15.

( ) 16.

( ) 17.

SUPPLEMENTARY DATA

	GRADE OR LEVEL	PROGRAM OR COURSE OF STUDY	TEXTS IN USE*	MINUTES PER WEEK	RANGE OF CLASS SIZE	TOTAL GRADE ENROLLMENT
	K					
Primary	1					
	2					
	3					
Intermediate	4					
	5					
	6					
Upper	7					
	8					

* List title briefly; include publisher and copyright date.

EVALUATIONS

( ) a. To what extent is the mathematics program structured to meet the needs of students in grades K through 8?

( ) b. To what extent is provision made for the mathematically gifted students?

( ) c. To what extent is provision made for remedial instruction?

( ) d. To what extent is the program a contemporary mathematics program?

( ) e. To what extent is the program articulated with the mathematics programs within the school, with other elementary schools, and with secondary schools of the area?

COMMENTS

II. Nature of Offerings

CHECKLIST

The selection of the content of the elementary mathematics program is based upon:

(   ) 1. a sequential development of unifying concepts essential to an understanding of the structure and meaning of mathematics.

(   ) 2. common and individual needs of students, as well as their readiness to use mathematical processes.

(   ) 3. the use of precise terminology which reveals mathematical relationships.

(   ) 4. the need for inductive and deductive reasoning.

(   ) 5. the need for application of mathematical knowledge to problem solving.

(   ) 6. a structural approach to computational skills.

(   ) 7. a desire to foster attitudes of orderliness, accuracy, speed, creativity and respect for learning.

(   ) 8. the necessity of articulation within the school and with other schools of the community.

(   ) 9. a recognition of the future demands of a technological society.

(   ) 10.

The elementary mathematics program includes:

(   ) 11. the study of the concepts and language of sets as a basis for all mathematical learnings.

(   ) 12. a study of the decimal system of numeration.

(   ) 13. a contrast of the decimal number system with other number systems such as the Roman and Egyptian to discover patterns in place value.

(   ) 14. a study of the four fundamental operations involving whole numbers, decimals, and fractions.

(   ) 15. applications of the three properties of numbers; identity and zero elements.

(   ) 16. computation in numeration systems with bases other than ten.

(   ) 17. application of number sentences to problem solving.

(   ) 18. mental computation; approximation and estimation.

(   ) 19. a study of rational numbers; positive and negative integers.

(   ) 20. a study of the concepts and applications of ratios and per cents.

(   ) 21. a development of measurement concepts; the metric system.

(   ) 22. an intepretation of and use of graphs and map scales.

(   ) 23. graphic construction and solution of equations and inequality sentences.

(   ) 24. an introduction to simple statistics and to probability.

(   ) 25. use of algebraic and geometric terminology and symbolism.

(   ) 26. a study of the fundamental concepts of algebra.

(   ) 27. identification and application of properties of plane and solid geometric figures.

(   ) 28. intuitive geometry; fundamental concepts of non-metric geometry.

(   ) 29. simple geometric constructions and verifications.

(   ) 30. simple informal and formal geometric proofs.

(   ) 31. a study of additional topics included in contemporary mathematics programs.

(   ) 32.

(   ) 33.

EVALUATIONS

(   ) a. To what extent is the mathematics curriculum sufficiently flexible to meet the needs of the students?
(   ) b. To what extent does the program develop understandings and appreciation of mathematics?
(   ) c. How successfully does the program prepare mathematically gifted students for future study of mathematics?
(   ) d. How adequately does the program prepare students to function competently in a highly technical society?
(   ) e. To what extent is there articulation with the other schools in the community?

COMMENTS

III. Physical Facilities

(   ) 1. The classroom provides adequate space for a variety of activities.

(   ) 2. The classroom is furnished with appropriate movable furniture.

(   ) 3. Adequate storage space is provided.

(   ) 4. The classroom is equipped for the effective use of multi-sensory teaching aids.

(   ) 5. The following additional equipment is available:

_____ chalkboards

_____ graph chalkboard

_____ cork board, magnetic board, peg board

_____ appropriate holders for charts and other instructional material

_____ bookcases

_____ duplicating machine and supplies

_____ overhead projector

_____ filmstrip projector

_____ movie projector

_____ television

_____

_____

(   ) *a. To what extent is there adequate space provision for existing class sizes?*

(   ) *b. To what extent is equipment adequate to meet student and curriculum needs?*

(   ) *c. To what extent is provision made for effective use of multi-sensory teaching aids?*

IV. Direction of Learning

A. INSTRUCTIONAL STAFF

CHECKLIST

Teachers of mathematics in the elementary school have:
(   ) 1. a broad liberal education.
(   ) 2. a knowledge of basic mathematical concepts.
(   ) 3. a knowledge of modern algebra and geometry.
(   ) 4. professional preparation for the teaching of mathematics in the elementary school.

Departmental teachers of mathematics have:
(   ) 5. a concentration in the field of mathematics.

The teachers of mathematics:
(   ) 6. manifest professional competency.
(   ) 7. obtain help from resource persons in the area.

(   ) 8. share experiences with other mathematics teachers in the area.

(   ) 9. modernize their preparation by enrolling in refresher courses, participating in workshops, and attending professional meetings.

(   ) 10. participate in faculty or departmental meetings to insure proper coordination of the total mathematics program.

(   ) 11.

(   ) 12.

EVALUATIONS

(   ) *a. To what extent is the preparation of the mathematics teachers adequate?*
(   ) *b. To what extent do the teachers exhibit professional competence in the area of mathematics?*
(   ) *c. To what extent do teachers utilize opportunities for professional growth?*

COMMENTS

IV. Direction of Learning

B. INSTRUCTIONAL ACTIVITIES

CHECKLIST

Instructional activities in mathematics:

( ) 1. are planned to realize the objectives of the school.

( ) 2. are organized to meet the specific objectives of the mathematics program.

( ) 3. reflect awareness of recent trends.

( ) 4. evidence pupil participation in planning, selecting and conducting class activities.

( ) 5. show systematic organization in planning and preparation.

( ) 6. provide for varying abilities of students by grouping or other means.

( ) 7. encourage scientific thinking through methods of discovery and inquiry.

( ) 8. provide for meaningful practice in computation.

( ) 9. are correlated with other subjects of the curriculum.

( ) 10. utilize resources of the community to enrich mathematics instruction.

( ) 11. include the use of manipulative materials, charts, and other aids.

( ) 12. are designed to prepare students for secondary school mathematics programs.

( ) 13.

( ) 14.

EVALUATIONS

( ) *a. To what extent do instructional activities contribute to the attainment of the objectives of the mathematics program?*

( ) *b. To what extent do instructional activities meet the needs of individual students?*

( ) *c. To what extent is there evidence of systematic planning and preparation in instructional activities?*

( ) *d. To what extent does the program articulate with programs offered in local elementary and secondary schools?*

COMMENTS

IV. Direction of Learning

C. INSTRUCTIONAL MATERIALS

CHECKLIST

(   ) 1. Mathematics textbooks evidence an awareness of new trends.

(   ) 2. Textbook selection is based on objectives of the mathematics program and is made after an intensive study by a competent professional committee.

(   ) 3. A copy of the basic text is provided for each student.

(   ) 4. Adequate reference materials are available and accessible.

(   ) 5. Current professional periodicals are available and accessible.

(   ) 6. Files containing testing and resource materials on mathematics are available and accessible.

(   ) 7. The following additional materials are available:

_____ ruler, compass, protractor -manipulative materials for the teaching of the numeration system, such as the abacus, number line, etc.

_____ fraction kit

_____ measure for linear dimension, metric measures, and liquid measures

_____ sample of plane figures

_____ models of cones, prisms, spheres, pyramids

_____

_____

EVALUATIONS

(   ) *a. To what extent has an adequate selection of materials been provided?*

(   ) *b. To what extent have the instructional materials been utilized?*

(   ) *c. To what extent are current materials and periodicals utilized?*

COMMENTS

IV. Direction of Learning

D. METHODS OF EVALUATION

CHECKLIST

(   )   1. The program of evaluation is organized in terms of the objectives of the elementary curriculum.

(   )   2. Tests are utilized to evaluate understandings as well as computational skills.

(   )   3. Attitudes and habits which result from instruction in mathematics are evaluated.

(   )   4. Various types of tests, including standardized and teacher-made tests, are a part of the evaluation program.

(   )   5. Evaluation of the program includes performance analysis derived from sources other than written tests.

(   )   6. Evaluation techniques measure quantitative vocabulary and analytic reading ability.

(   )   7. Evaluation identifies students for classification in specialized programs.

(   )   8. Evaluation identifies creativity.

(   )   9. Self-evaluation by students is encouraged.

(   ) 10. The evaluation program is both continuous and periodic.

(   ) 11. Services of professional, competent individuals are engaged for test interpretation.

(   ) 12. Results of evaluation procedures are utilized to improve the mathematics program.

(   ) 13.

(   ) 14.

EVALUATIONS

(   )   a. *How adequate is the evaluation program?*

(   )   b. *To what extent are the results of evaluation available to the faculty for diagnostic, prognostic, and guidance purposes?*

(   )   c. *To what extent are the results of evaluation used in improving the mathematics program?*

COMMENTS

V. Outcomes

EVALUATIONS

(   ) *a. To what extent do students demonstrate an understanding of the structure of mathematics?*
(   ) *b. To what extent does the mathematics program meet the needs of students?*
(   ) *c. To what degree is an attitude of inquiry and discovery encouraged?*
(   ) *d. To what extent do students show competence in understanding and solving problems?*
(   ) *e. To what extent are computational skills employed to achieve mastery of basic concepts?*
(   ) *f. How adequate is the students' use of precise terminology of contemporary mathematics?*
(   ) *g. To what degree do students manifest interest in mathematics?*

VI. Special Characteristics of Mathematics

1. In what areas has the greatest success been achieved in the mathematics program?

   a.

   b.

   c.

   d.

   e.

2. In what areas should the program be strengthened?

   a.

   b.

   c.

   d.

   e.

   f.

VII. General Evaluation of Instruction in Mathematics

EVALUATIONS

(   ) *a. To what extent has the program in mathematics achieved the objectives and conformed with the philosophy of the school as set forth in Section B?*
(   ) *b. To what extent has the program in mathematics met the needs of students as set forth in Section C?*
(   ) *c. To what extent has the school analyzed its weaknesses in mathematics and taken measures to remedy them?*

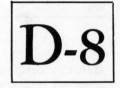

D-8

Formulated and Edited by the Criteria Committee, Elementary School
Department of The National Catholic Educational Association

Music

GUIDING PRINCIPLES

The music program in the elementary school has for its basic principle the cultivation of the student's love of music. Experiences which develop understandings, skills and appreciations in all students are provided. These contribute to the emotional and social development of personality, help to discipline the intellect, provide opportunities for the experience of beauty, and enable the students to praise God in sung worship.

Finally, the music program is designed to discover and encourage exceptional music aptitude and abilities.

NAME OF SCHOOL_____ DATE_____

ADDRESS_____

(ARCH)DIOCESE OF_____

SELF-EVALUATION MEMBERS_____

_____

_____

Instructions

When undertaking a self-evaluation the members of the school staff should use the statement of GUIDING PRINCIPLES and CHECKLIST items as an aid to determining the extent to which their school program coincides with the Philosophy and Objectives of the school and meets the needs of the school population and community served. Of necessity a staff will modify statements of Guiding Principles, Checklist items and Evaluations to conform with the philosophy and characteristics of the particular school doing the evaluation. Wherever changes are made the school should explain under Comments the reasons for the change in relation to its own program. Minor differences in terminology should not be regarded as significant items of change.

CHECKLISTS

Checklist items consist of statements deemed applicable to the area of the Criteria being evaluated. These are suggested ideas and are not to be interpreted as the only statements applicable to the area or as all-inclusive. A school may wish to add additional statements of its own that will explain further the particular program of the school. Space is provided in each Checklist for such additions. If the change is regarded as significant, the school will use the letter C in the Checklist as indicated in the following instructions and explain under Comments the precise nature of its offerings.

A staff should note that a definite relation pertains between Checklist items and Evaluations. Members of the staff should familiarize themselves with the definite meanings of Checklist symbols and Evaluation ratings.

CHECKLIST items may be indicated as follows:

E—The statement or condition is *extensive* in application.

M—The statement or condition is *moderately* achieved.

L—The statement or condition is limited in application.

MN—The condition is missing but judged needed by the staff.

N—The condition does not apply to this school.

*C—The condition is achieved in a manner different from Checklist items.

    * Wherever C is used, this aim should be stated in one of the additional numbers of the Checklist and explained under COMMENTS.

EVALUATIONS

Evaluations represent numerical summations of the Checklist items. The rating is determined from discussions of the staff as related to the consistency of the school program with stated Philosophy and Objectives.

To secure a composite view of the school's outcomes in each area of the Criteria, a school will project the Evaluation ratings to the X Blank of the respective areas. A further picture of the total program will be secured by tabulating the Average of the X Blank on the Graphic Summary provided in the Y Blank. Instructions for such procedure are listed in the X and Y Blanks.

Evaluations are indicated as follows:

5—The condition is excellent and extensive. (Please note that 5 does not mean "perfect.")

4—The condition is very good. A school may care to use a further refinement of 4a or 4b: 4a indicates that the condition is extensive and functioning well; 4b indicates that the condition is moderately extensive but functioning excellently.

3—The condition meets student needs to a reasonable degree.

2—The condition is in need of *achievable* improvement.

1—The condition is not being achieved and its need is not recognized.

*MN—The condition is missing but needed.

 *N—The condition does not apply.

    * When MN or N are accepted by the staff for an *Evaluation* rating the divisor on the X Blank must be adjusted accordingly. N should not be used in CHECKLISTS and EVALUATIONS unless the condition absolutely DOES NOT APPLY. If the item is educationally desirable the school should not use N simply because it does not make use of the item. An adequate replacement for the item may fulfill the conditions of the Checklist.

I. Organization

(   ) 1. Music is an integral part of the curriculum.

(   ) 2. Music is taught in a suitable environment.

(   ) 3. Time allotment for music instruction is adequate.

(   ) 4. Schedule provides for departmental teaching of music.

(   ) 5. Music activities outside the regular music programs are available.

(   ) 6. Talented students are encouraged to study music privately.

(   ) 7. Music ensembles and individual students have opportunities to participate in school-sponsored programs and assemblies.

(   ) 8. The school cooperates with other schools and with community groups in joint musical programs.

(   ) 9. The elementary music program is articulated with that of the secondary school.

(   ) 10.

(   ) 11.

SUPPLEMENTARY DATA

Title of Text	Grade or Level	Enrollment	No. of Sections	Range of Class Size	Minutes per Week

1. Percentage of students participating in music festivals or programs during the previous year........———————

2. Number of special teachers of music...———————

3. Number of classroom teachers engaged in teaching music ....·———————

4. Total number of teachers in school.....................................·———————

5. Total enrollment ....·———————

EVALUATIONS

(   ) a. *To what extent does the program provide music instruction for all students?*

(   ) b. *To what extent does the program provide for talented students?*

(   ) c. *To what extent do time allotments for music meet the demands of the program?*

(   ) d. *To what extent does the school participate in community musical programs?*

II. Nature of Offerings

CHECKLIST

I. The vocal music program:

(   ) 1. provides vocal training for students.

(   ) 2. provides adequate song material, including folk music and music of great composers.

(   ) 3. provides adequate training for changing voices.

(   ) 4. provides for sight-reading.

(   ) 5. provides instruction in functional music theory.

(   ) 6. provides instruction and practice in part-singing.

(   ) 7.

(   ) 8.

II. The liturgical music program:

(   ) 1. provides adequate instruction and practice in sacred music.

(   ) 2. provides opportunities for students to participate in the sung liturgy.

(   ) 3. provides instruction in the theory of Gregorian Chant.

(   ) 4. coordinates instruction in the theory of Gregorian Chant with instruction in the theory of modern music.

(   ) 5.

(   ) 6.

III. The program of music appreciation:

(   ) 1. provides for listening in connection with the regular music courses.

(   ) 2. is adequately served by a record library.

(   ) 3. provides for occasional attendance at good concerts.

(   ) 4. arranges for professional performing groups to come to the school.

(   ) 5.

(   ) 6.

IV. The program of instructional music:

(   ) 1. includes a school orchestra and/or band.

(   ) 2. provides opportunities for students to take lessons on band or orchestra instruments.

(   ) 3. provides opportunities for students to take piano lessons.

(   ) 4. includes instruction in pre-band melody and percussion instruments at primary level.

(   ) 5.

(   ) 6.

EVALUATIONS

(   ) a. *How adequate is the vocal music program?*

(   ) b. *How adequate is the liturgical music program?*

(   ) c. *How adequate is the program of music appreciation?*

(   ) d. *How adequate is the instrumental music program?*

(   ) e. *How well are music activities adapted to student needs?*

COMMENTS

III. Physical Facilities

CHECKLIST

(   ) 1. Classrooms are properly designed and equipped for music instruction.

(   ) 2. Music rooms are properly designed and equipped.

(   ) 3. Seating for vocal and instrumental classes is comfortable and suitable.

(   ) 4. School-owned instruments are properly serviced.

(   ) 5. Adequate and convenient storage space is provided.

(   ) 6. The following equipment is available: (check)

     _____ piano

     _____ organ

     _____ record player

     _____ staff liners

     _____ records to accompany textbooks

     _____ records for appreciation

     _____ tape recorder

     _____ pre-band melody and percussion instruments

     _____ autoharp

     _____ music stands

     _____ portable risers

     _____ podium

(   ) 7.

(   ) 8.

EVALUATIONS

(   ) *a. Are the classrooms adequate for music instruction?*

(   ) *b. Is the music equipment adequate?*

COMMENTS

IV. Direction of Learning

A. INSTRUCTIONAL STAFF

CHECKLIST

The professional preparation of teachers responsible for the music program includes:

(   ) 1. liberal education.

(   ) 2. background in music theory and piano.

(   ) 3. preparation for teaching vocal music.

(   ) 4. courses in music methods.

(   ) 5. preparation for teaching instrumental music.

(   ) 6. interest in continuing education by attendance at workshops, etc.

(   ) 7. membership in professional organizations serving music education.

(   ) 8.

(   ) 9.

EVALUATIONS

(   ) *a. How adequate is the professional background of the staff?*

(   ) *b. How adequate is the preparation of the staff for teaching music?*

(   ) *c. How adequate is the preparation of the staff for teaching instrumental music?*

COMMENTS

B. INSTRUCTIONAL ACTIVITIES

CHECKLIST

(   ) 1. Music instruction is carefully planned by teachers.

(   ) 2. Instruction includes music theory.

(   ) 3. Instruction integrates sacred and secular music.

(   ) 4. Music instruction is integrated with other academic subjects.

(   ) 5. Supervision is provided by visits of music consultant or supervisor.

(   ) 6.

(   ) 7.

EVALUATIONS

(   ) *a. How adequate is preparation for daily music lessons?*

(   ) *b. How effectively is music taught?*

(   ) *c. To what extent is music integrated with the general curriculum?*

(   ) *d. How adequate is the supervision of music instruction?*

COMMENTS

C. INSTRUCTIONAL MATERIALS

( ) 1. Supply of music texts is adequate.

( ) 2. Texts provide instruction in sacred and secular music.

( ) 3. Visual aids are adequate.

( ) 4. Slides and/or filmstrips and projector are available.

( ) 5. Instrumental groups are provided with adequate scores.

( ) 6. Records for appreciation and teaching are available.

( ) 7.

( ) 8.

EVALUATIONS

( ) a. *How adequate is the quantity of instructional materials?*

( ) b. *How suitable is the quality of instructional materials?*

( ) c. *How extensive is the variety of instructional materials?*

COMMENTS

D. METHODS OF EVALUATION

CHECKLIST

( ) 1. Evaluative procedures are designed to measure progress in musical undertanding.

( ) 2. Quality of vocal training is evaluated.

( ) 3. Tape recordings are used to evaluate individual and group performances.

( ) 4. Individual differences in musical aptitude are considered.

( ) 5. Tests are used to determine musical talent.

( ) 6.

( ) 7.

EVALUATIONS

( ) a. *How adequately do evaluation procedures measure effectiveness of instruction?*

( ) b. *How well does the testing program identify musically talented students?*

COMMENTS

V. Outcomes

(   ) *a. To what extent do students appreciate the special function of liturgical music?*
(   ) *b. To what extent do students perform liturgical music?*
(   ) *c. How adequately does the program develop the musical understanding of students?*
(   ) *d. To what extent do students develop skill in singing?*
(   ) *e. To what extent do students develop skill in reading music?*
(   ) *f. To what extent do students develop skill in playing instruments?*
(   ) *g. To what extent do students perform in ensemble?*
(   ) *h. To what extent do students show an appreciation of music?*
(   ) *i. To what extent does the program identify and develop special music talent?*

VI. Special Characteristics

1. In what areas is music instruction competent and efficient?

    a.

    b.

    c.

    d.

    e.

2. In what areas is there need for improving the music program?

    a.

    b.

    c.

    d.

    e.

VII. General Evaluation

(   ) *a. To what extent is instruction in music consistent with the philosophy of the school?*
(   ) *b. To what extent does the music program serve the needs of the students?*
(   ) *c. To what extent does the school recognize its problems in music instruction and set about solving them?*

Formulated and Edited by the Criteria Committee, Elementary School
Department of The National Catholic Educational Association

Religion

GUIDING PRINCIPLES

Christian education strives to deepen love of God and neighbor in the individual and to express this love in right relationships in the home, school, parish, social and civil societies. This is accomplished under the guardianship of the Church through the inspiration of grace. The total program in religion includes a developmental study of religious truths and of Sacred Scripture, participation in worship, practice in Christlike living, and growth in self-knowledge. As the learner responds in faith and trust to his Christian heritage, he becomes a vital member of the Church.

From a solid biblical, liturgical, and catechetical formation come ever-deepening understandings, more wholesome attitudes and more responsible patterns of action. Christian ethics must be cultivated by daily teaching and learning which gradually intensify the grasp of principles and turn knowledge into reasoned conviction. Through its practical application, religion is the integrating force in the Catholic school and gives the school its unique significance.

Hence the study of religion must be serious and penetrating, complete and comprehensive. A satisfactory religion program is distinguished by a continued critical analysis of the perception of sacred truths and of the effect religious commitment has on the individual and on the total life of the school. The program in worship and service is evaluated more specifically in Section E, "Student Activity Program," and Section G, "Guidance Services."

The religion program has for its end the true and perfect Christian, the integrated personality and character. This end results from continuing religious education by means of which the human person encounters the divine Person. As this God-centered orientation takes place, the result in terms of religious living is a concern for the Kingdom of God and for the welfare of all mankind. When this integration is accomplished, Christian ethics is rooted in minds, wills and souls. These existential relationships with God and man are the environment in which Christian education takes place.

NAME OF SCHOOL_____ DATE_____

ADDRESS_____

(ARCH)DIOCESE OF_____

SELF-EVALUATION MEMBERS_____

_____

_____

Instructions

When undertaking a self-evaluation the members of the school staff should use the statement of GUIDING PRINCIPLES and CHECKLIST items as an aid to determining the extent to which their school program coincides with the Philosophy and Objectives of the school and meets the needs of the school population and community served. Of necessity a staff will modify statements of Guiding Principles, Checklist items and Evaluations to conform with the philosophy and characteristics of the particular school doing the evaluation. Wherever changes are made the school should explain under Comments the reasons for the change in relation to its own program. Minor differences in terminology should not be regarded as significant items of change.

CHECKLISTS

Checklist items consist of statements deemed applicable to the area of the Criteria being evaluated. These are suggested ideas and are not to be interpreted as the only statements applicable to the area or as all-inclusive. A school may wish to add additional statements of its own that will explain further the particular program of the school. Space is provided in each Checklist for such additions. If the change is regarded as significant, the school will use the letter C in the Checklist as indicated in the following instructions and explain under Comments the precise nature of its offerings.

A staff should note that a definite relation pertains between Checklist items and Evaluations. Members of the staff should familiarize themselves with the definite meanings of Checklist symbols and Evaluation ratings.

CHECKLIST items may be indicated as follows:

E—The statement or condition is *extensive* in application.

M—The statement or condition is *moderately* achieved.

L—The statement or condition is limited in application.

MN—The condition is missing but judged needed by the staff.

N—The condition does not apply to this school.

*C—The condition is achieved in a manner different from Checklist items.

* Wherever C is used, this aim should be stated in one of the additional numbers of the Checklist and explained under COMMENTS.

EVALUATIONS

Evaluations represent numerical summations of the Checklist items. The rating is determined from discussions of the staff as related to the consistency of the school program with stated Philosophy and Objectives.

To secure a composite view of the school's outcomes in each area of the Criteria, a school will project the Evaluation ratings to the X Blank of the respective areas. A further picture of the total program will be secured by tabulating the Average of the X Blank on the Graphic Summary provided in the Y Blank. Instructions for such procedure are listed in the X and Y Blanks.

Evaluations are indicated as follows:

5—The condition is excellent and extensive. (Please note that 5 does not mean "perfect.")

4—The condition is very good. A school may care to use a further refinement of 4a or 4b: 4a indicates that the condition is extensive and functioning well; 4b indicates that the condition is moderately extensive but functioning excellently.

3—The condition meets student needs to a reasonable degree.

2—The condition is in need of *achievable* improvement.

1—The condition is not being achieved and its need is not recognized.

*MN—The condition is missing but needed.

*N—The condition does not apply.

* When MN or N are accepted by the staff for an *Evaluation* rating the divisor on the X Blank must be adjusted accordingly. N should not be used in CHECKLISTS and EVALUATIONS unless the condition absolutely DOES NOT APPLY. If the item is educationally desirable the school should not use N simply because it does not make use of the item. An adequate replacement for the item may fulfill the conditions of the Checklist.

I. Organization

( ) 1. A definite program in religion is followed:
(check) diocesan _____
community _____
other _____

Religion programs are:

( ) 2. required of all students.

( ) 3. scheduled regularly:
a. number of periods per week _____
b. length of periods:
(1) kindergarten:
_____ minutes
(2) primary grades:
_____ minutes
(3) intermediate:
_____ minutes
(4) upper grades:
_____ minutes

( ) 4. scheduled in accordance with diocesan time allotment.

( ) 5. regarded as an integral part of the instruction program.

( ) 6. planned as a unified whole.

( ) 7. correlated wisely with other subject areas in each grade.

( ) 8. related to other religious activities in the school.

( ) 9. related to religious activities in home, parish, and community.

( ) 10. revised in the light of current developments sanctioned by the Magisterium of the Church.

Opportunities are provided for:

( ) 11. voluntary participation in religious activities, particularly Mass, the reception of the sacraments, and prayer.

( ) 12. the practice of the natural virtues as the bases for the supernatural.

( ) 13. the practice of the theological and moral virtues.

( ) 14. the practice of the spiritual and corporal works of mercy.

( ) 15. the use of talents of students in developing the above practices.

( ) 16. counseling on religious matters for students and teachers.

( ) 17.

( ) 18.

( ) a. *To what extent are programs in religion provided?*

( ) b. *How appropriate is the allotment of time for the religion program?*

( ) c. *How well is instruction in religion integrated with other programs and activities?*

( ) d. *To what extent do programs in religion incorporate current developments sanctioned by the Magisterium of the Church?*

( ) e. *Are the opportunities for religious activities designed to meet the recognized needs of students?*

( ) f. *How effectively is the religion program related to the daily life of students?*

( ) g. *How adequately is provision made for counseling on religious matters?*

II. Nature of Offerings

CHECKLIST (*Add any important items which are not included below.*)

Instruction in religion teaches a clear and consistent philosophy or approach to:

( ) 1. the nature of God.
( ) 2. the nature of Redemption.
( ) 3. the nature of revelation.
( ) 4. the nature of the Church.
( ) 5. the nature of beliefs and practices.

Instruction in religion includes the teaching of religious truths and moral principles which:

( ) 6. foster in the students a consciousness of God and a sense of personal relationship and trust in Him.
( ) 7. outline the individual's personal responsibilities to God.
( ) 8. inculcate in the student a sense of personal relationship and responsibility to his fellowman.
( ) 9. afford intellectual grasp through reasoned explanation of the teaching of faith.
( ) 10. lead the student to a Christian interpretation of life and the ability to see God's plan in it.
( ) 11. give the student an understanding of the Church and his place in it.
( ) 12. stress moral and ethical conduct in private and public life.
( ) 13. demonstrate the religious basis for good citizenship, social justice and personal responsibility.
( ) 14. demonstrate that a spiritually vital parish united with its bishop is the chief instrument for growth in Christian life.
( ) 15. develop an appreciation of the importance of the Christian family, and the need for contributing to its spiritual and temporal welfare.
( ) 16. emphasize the authority of God expressed through parents, teachers, and other lawful agents.

Instruction in religion includes content and experiences which:

( ) 17. recognize varied developmental age levels of students.
( ) 18. provide an adequate religious background for the student.
( ) 19. correlate with other subject areas in the curriculum.
( ) 20. provide help to each student in forming a unified plan of life for present and future living.
( ) 21. inculcate a knowledge and appreciation of Sacred Scripture.
( ) 22. familiarize the students with other types of religious literature.
( ) 23. give knowledge of the sacraments.
( ) 24. encourage participation in the sacred liturgy.
( ) 25. teach the Mass as the center of Christian life and worship.
( ) 26. give knowledge of the heritage of the Church: doctrine, movements, history, trends, arts, and missionary endeavors.
( ) 27. prepare the student to respect the religious beliefs of others.
( ) 28. enable the student to communicate knowledge of his faith to others.
( ) 29. help the student choose the vocation in which he will best serve God and man and develop his own potentialities.
( ) 30. emphasize the role of the parish in Christian living.

( ) 31.

( ) 32.

EVALUATIONS

( ) a. *How adequate is the content of the offerings in terms of the religious needs of students?*
( ) b. *How effective is the religion program in leading to a personal consciousness of God as a reality?*
( ) c. *How effective is the religion program in providing the student with a sound basis for present and future Christian social living?*
( ) d. *How well is the religion program correlated with other subjects?*
( ) e. *How thoroughly does the religion program prepare the student to recognize and fulfill his role as an active, vital member of the Church?*

COMMENTS

III. Physical Facilities

CHECKLIST

( ) 1. Classrooms conform to educational standards for the age group.

( ) 2. Classroom furnishings are suitable.

( ) 3. Classrooms are equipped for a variety of uses.

( ) 4. A church or chapel is available for use of students and services.

( ) 5. Religious symbols in keeping with good taste are present in the building.

( ) 6. Classroom facilities and equipment are available for use of the Confraternity of Christian Doctrine.

( ) 7.

( ) 8.

EVALUATIONS

( ) *a. How satisfactory are the physical facilities in meeting the instructional needs of the program?*

( ) *b. How satisfactory are external evidences of the Catholic faith?*

( ) *c. How satisfactory are the facilities provided for the Confraternity of Christian Doctrine?*

COMMENTS

IV. Direction of Learning

A. INSTRUCTION STAFF

(For data on preparation of teachers, see Section K, "Individual Staff Members.")

CHECKLIST

Members of the staff:

( ) 1. have adequate background in the content of religion.

( ) 2. consult experts in the field of religion.

( ) 3. participate in selecting instructional materials.

( ) 4. are prepared in current catechesis.

( ) 5. have competence in religious education.

( ) 6. relate religion wisely with other subjects.

( ) 7. teach the major religious truths in depth.

( ) 8. foster a love for God in the students in order to bring about an effective encounter with Him.

( ) 9. guide the religious reading programs of the students.

( ) 10. apply the teaching methods of Christ.

( ) 11. are attentive to see Christ in each student.

( ) 12. maintain a joyful atmosphere in religion classes.

( ) 13. are strong in their faith and respectful of the faith of others.

( ) 14. participate in the liturgy of the Church.

( ) 15. discuss periodically the effectiveness of the religion program and reexamine the statement of purpose.

( ) 16.

( ) 17.

EVALUATIONS

( ) *a. How adequately is the staff prepared in the content of religion?*

( ) *b. How adequately is the staff prepared in methods of teaching religion?*

( ) *c. How adequately do members of the staff integrate religion with other subjects?*

( ) *d. How effectively do members of the staff show the value of religion through their efforts and example?*

( ) *e. How adequately does the staff evaluate the effectiveness of its program?*

COMMENTS

B. INSTRUCTIONAL ACTIVITIES

CHECKLIST

Many aspects are considered in planning instructional activities.

( ) 1. Teachers consider the student's:
_____ spiritual and bodily powers.
_____ social nature.
_____ needs and interests.
_____ degree of maturity.
_____ personal experiences.

( ) 2. The truths of religious instruction are related to:
_____ home life.
_____ personal problems.
_____ previous instruction.
_____ other religious activities.
_____ problems of school.
_____ problems of community.
_____ current trends in the Church.

_____

( ) 3. Time is given students for spiritual reflection.

( ) 4. Teachers provide opportunities for individual conferences.

( ) 5. Provision is made for members of the clergy to supplement the teaching of the regular staff.

( ) 6. Opportunities are made available for voluntary religious worship: Mass, reception of the Sacraments, _____
_____
_____

( ) 7. Opportunities are provided for student involvement and leadership in religious organizations devoted to charity and service, such as: Sodalities, Junior Holy Name Society, Propagation of the Faith, _____
_____
_____
_____
_____

( ) 8. Teachers correlate their work with that of other subjects.

( ) 9. Opportunities are provided for the practice of the spiritual and corporal works of mercy.

( ) 10. Stress is placed on application of religious truths and principles to the personal lives of the students.

( ) 11.

( ) 12.

EVALUATIONS

( ) a. *How effectively is instruction in religion planned in relation to objectives of the school?*
( ) b. *How adequately is instruction related to the needs of the individual student?*
( ) c. *How adequately is instruction related to the total school program?*
( ) d. *How adequately do the out-of-school activities of the students reflect Christ-like personalities?*
( ) e. *How effective is the teaching for leadership and apostolic activity?*

COMMENTS

C. INSTRUCTIONAL MATERIALS

(Use the symbols, E, M, C, L, MN, N as stated on instruction sheet to check instructional materials listed below.)

CHECKLIST

MATERIALS	APPROPRIATE TO THE AGE, INTELLIGENCE AND EMOTIONAL LEVELS OF THE STUDENTS	INTELLECTUAL AND ESTHETIC QUALITY OF WORKS USED	APPLICATION TO CHRISTIAN LIVING
Bibles			
New Testaments			
Missals			
Textbooks			
Reference books			
Current literature			
Catholic newspapers			
Devotional reading			
Biographies			
Periodicals			
Plays			
Poetry			
Music			
Charts			
Art Forms			
Filmstrips			
Films			
Transparencies			
Slides			
Records			
Tapes			

( ) Instructional materials are consistent with the expressed philosophy of the school.

EVALUATIONS

( ) a. To what extent are instructional materials consistent with the philosophy of the school?
( ) b. How practical are the instructional materials?
( ) c. How complete and current are instructional materials?
( ) d. How effectively are the students guided in the use of these materials?

COMMENTS

D. METHODS OF EVALUATION

CHECKLIST

(   ) 1. Oral and written examinations (essay and objective tests) are used in evaluating instruction.

(   ) 2. Individual conferences are used in evaluating attitudes toward religion.

(   ) 3. Reaction of students to problems and situations reflect their degree of moral awareness.

(   ) 4. The students' understanding of religious principles is shown by their application of these ideals in school life.

(   ) 5. Students appraise their progress in applying principles of religion to social and civic life.

(   ) 6. Parents and teachers confer to evaluate students' progress in applying religious principles.

(   ) 7. Students spread their faith by word and example.

(   ) 8. Parish data are utilized in evaluating the effectiveness of the program in religion.

(   ) 9. The school has a follow-up plan through which success of the religion program can be estimated.

(   ) 10. Teachers and students recognize the limitations of testing in religion and the impossibility of evaluating all the desirable outcomes of religious instruction.

(   ) 11.

(   ) 12.

EVALUATIONS

(   ) a. How adequate are appraisal procedures in evaluating the religion program?

(   ) b. To what extent do teachers use the results of evaluation to judge the quality of instruction?

(   ) c. How well does evaluation identify the individual who needs further help?

(   ) d. How well do students spread their faith by word and example?

(   ) e. How consistent are evaluation procedures with the basic philosophy of the school?

COMMENTS

V. Outcomes

(No checklist items are prepared for this division since they would be largely repetitious of checklist items in preceding divisions.)

EVALUATIONS

(   ) a. *How well have the students mastered the content in religion?*
(   ) b. *To what degree do religious principles, ideals and insights appear to function in the lives of the students?*
(   ) c. *How effective is religious leadership among students?*
(   ) d. *To what extent do students willingly participate in religious activities?*
(   ) e. *How fully are students awakened to moral issues in life?*
(   ) f. *How consistent are students' habits with religious instruction?*
(   ) g. *To what extent do students manifest prudence in choosing companionship in recreation?*
(   ) h. *What evidences are there of apostolic endeavor in the service of God and man?*
(   ) i. *To what extent are students familiar with the Bible?*
(   ) j. *How effectively do students participate in the liturgy?*
(   ) k. *To what extent are students free to express feelings and opinions?*
(   ) l. *What is the usual percentage of individual student participation during religious instruction?*
(   ) m. *What evidence is there that students seek ways to work out Christian solutions for their most pressing personal problems?*
(   ) n. *Are students giving indications of progress in prayer?*

VI. Special Characteristics of Religion Program

1. The religion program is most commendable and satisfactory in the following respects:

   a.

   b.

   c.

   d.

2. The greatest needs for strengthening instruction in religion are:

   a.

   b.

   c.

   d.

VII. General Evaluation of Instruction in Religion

EVALUATIONS

(   ) a. *How adequately does instruction in religion reflect the philosophy and objectives embodied in Section B?*
(   ) b. *How adequately does instruction in religion provide for student needs as expressed in Section C?*
(   ) c. *How adequately does the school identify problems in religious instruction and seek their solution?*
(   ) d. *How adequately does the student participate in the active life of the parish?*

Formulated and Edited by the Criteria Committee, Elementary School
Department of The National Catholic Educational Association

Science

GUIDING PRINCIPLES

A study of science on the elementary level should include knowledge and understandings, activities and experiences structured to meet the educational needs of the students. It should be planned to arouse and sustain interest, to develop desirable attitudes and sincere appreciation for the things in nature which have been wisely provided by God and scientifically developed by man for better material living.

Provision for systematic learning should be designed to meet the needs and interests of all students. Learning activities should be focused on group and individual needs, abilities, and interests.

Extension of understandings should be stimulated through research reading, laboratory investigation, and visual aids. Organization of materials and methods of instruction should guide the learner to discover truth intuitively from group and individual observations and experience.

Content should be such that the student can study it in areas of daily living in the home, school, and community. It should aid students in strengthening their relations to nature, in assuming their places in the world of continued scientific research, and in giving added meaning to the goals of Christian living.

NAME OF SCHOOL_____ DATE_____

ADDRESS_____

(ARCH)DIOCESE OF_____

SELF-EVALUATION MEMBERS_____

_____

_____

Instructions

When undertaking a self-evaluation the members of the school staff should use the statement of GUIDING PRINCIPLES and CHECKLIST items as an aid to determining the extent to which their school program coincides with the Philosophy and Objectives of the school and meets the needs of the school population and community served. Of necessity a staff will modify statements of Guiding Principles, Checklist items and Evaluations to conform with the philosophy and characteristics of the particular school doing the evaluation. Wherever changes are made the school should explain under Comments the reasons for the change in relation to its own program. Minor differences in terminology should not be regarded as significant items of change.

CHECKLISTS

Checklist items consist of statements deemed applicable to the area of the Criteria being evaluated. These are suggested ideas and are not to be interpreted as the only statements applicable to the area or as all-inclusive. A school may wish to add additional statements of its own that will explain further the particular program of the school. Space is provided in each Checklist for such additions. If the change is regarded as significant, the school will use the letter C in the Checklist as indicated in the following instructions and explain under Comments the precise nature of its offerings.

A staff should note that a definite relation pertains between Checklist items and Evaluations. Members of the staff should familiarize themselves with the definite meanings of Checklist symbols and Evaluation ratings.

CHECKLIST items may be indicated as follows:

E—The statement or condition is *extensive* in application.

M—The statement or condition is *moderately* achieved.

L—The statement or condition is limited in application.

MN—The condition is missing but judged needed by the staff.

N—The condition does not apply to this school.

*C—The condition is achieved in a manner different from Checklist items.

* Wherever C is used, this aim should be stated in one of the additional numbers of the Checklist and explained under COMMENTS.

EVALUATIONS

Evaluations represent numerical summations of the Checklist items. The rating is determined from discussions of the staff as related to the consistency of the school program with stated Philosophy and Objectives.

To secure a composite view of the school's outcomes in each area of the Criteria, a school will project the Evaluation ratings to the X Blank of the respective areas. A further picture of the total program will be secured by tabulating the Average of the X Blank on the Graphic Summary provided in the Y Blank. Instructions for such procedure are listed in the X and Y Blanks.

Evaluations are indicated as follows:.

5—The condition is excellent and extensive. (Please note that 5 does not mean "perfect.")

4—The condition is very good. A school may care to use a further refinement of 4a or 4b: 4a indicates that the condition is extensive and functioning well; 4b indicates that the condition is moderately extensive but functioning excellently.

3—The condition meets student needs to a reasonable degree.

2—The condition is in need of *achievable* improvement.

1—The condition is not being achieved and its need is not recognized.

*MN—The condition is missing but needed.

*N—The condition does not apply.

* When MN or N are accepted by the staff for an *Evaluation* rating the divisor on the X Blank must be adjusted accordingly. N should not be used in CHECKLISTS and EVALUATIONS unless the condition absolutely DOES NOT APPLY. If the item is educationally desirable the school should not use N simply because it does not make use of the item. An adequate replacement for the item may fulfill the conditions of the Checklist.

I. Organization of Science

CHECKLIST

(   )   1. A continuous developmental science program is provided in the school.

(   )   2. Opportunities are provided for all students to participate in science activities to meet their common needs and interests.

(   )   3. Opportunities for research are provided for students of scientific ability.

(   )   4. Opportunities for learning activities are provided for both group and individual instruction, experimentation, and investigation.

(   )   5. Opportunities are provided for students to construct and use simple home-made equipment and/or science kits.

(   )   6. Opportunities are provided for students to acquire scientific experiences through TV and/or outdoor laboratories.

(   )   7. Occasional field trips, museum, planetarium, industrial visits, and other experiences away from the classroom are part of the science program.

(   )   8. Provisions are made for teachers to help groups and individual students working on science projects.

(   )   9. The science program of studies is well-defined, sequential, and up-to-date.

(   ) 10. Presentation of content provides activities and experiments in which students discover facts, draw conclusions, and extend their understandings on their own.

(   ) 11. Articulation is made with the science program in the secondary schools.

(   ) 12.

(   ) 13.

SUPPLEMENTARY DATA

I. ORGANIZATION						
GRADE	ENROLLMENT	NO. OF SECTIONS	RANGE OF CLASS SIZE	MINUTES PER WEEK	WEEKS PER YEAR	TEACHER
Science Primary—						
Intermediate—						
Upper Elementary—						
General Science						

TEXTBOOK DATA

GRADE OR LEVEL	NAME OF TEXT	PUBLISHER	DATE OF PUBLICATION

EVALUATIONS

(   ) *a. To what extent is science provided for all students in the elementary school?*

(   ) *b. How extensive is the scope of instruction in order to meet the needs of the elementary school student?*

(   ) *c. To what extent do the time allotments for science satisfactorily meet instructional needs?*

(   ) *d. To what extent is articulation made with the secondary schools' science programs?*

(   ) *e. To what extent does the school utilize community resources?*

COMMENTS

II. Nature of Offerings

The instruction in science is designed to:

( ) 1. lead students into closer contact with nature through an awareness of their environment.

( ) 2. help students acquire a proper understanding of their relationship to God and fellow man, to self and nature.

( ) 3. aid students to recognize the dignity of man as the highest of all earthly creatures.

( ) 4. enable students to understand that resources, discoveries and inventions contribute to the conservation of natural and human resources.

( ) 5. develop habits of careful observation through simple experimentation with the materials in the students' environment.

( ) 6. challenge students with problem situations which force them to think, draw conclusions and to suggest solutions.

( ) 7. stress the acquisition of general science concepts which are suitable to the maturity level of the students.

( ) 8. provide opportunities for students to plan and construct apparatus and equipment.

( ) 9. provide opportunities for students to work individually and in groups on projects or problems of their own choice.

( ) 10. develop scientific attitudes, skills, knowledge, understandings, and appreciations.

( ) 11. develop a body of knowledge composed of interrelating facts, concepts, and principles.

( ) 12. acquaint students with current developments in science.

( ) 13.

( ) 14.

( ) *a. How adequate are the science offerings?*

( ) *b. To what extent do the science offerings meet the science needs of the students?*

III. Physical Facilities

CHECKLIST

The physical facilities for science include:

( ) 1. sufficient classroom space for discussion, work activities, demonstrations and experimentations, projects and discussions.
( ) 2. a demonstration table supplied with the necessary equipment.
( ) 3. preparation and storage area for the teacher.
( ) 4. student project area including work space and storage space.
( ) 5. space and equipment for the proper maintenance of animals and plants.
( ) 6. cork boards, peg boards, and bookshelves.
( ) 7. files for inventory, catalogs, tests, and other instructional materials.
( ) 8. easily accessible, well-stocked first-aid kit.
( ) 9. provisions for multi-sensory aids including TV.
( ) 10.
( ) 11.

EVALUATIONS

( ) a. *To what extent is classroom space provided for science instruction?*
( ) b. *How adequately furnished are the classrooms and/or laboratories for science teaching?*
( ) c. *How adequate are the equipment and materials?*
( ) d. *How adequate are storage facilities for equipment and supplies?*
( ) e. *How adequate are the provisions for student safety?*
( ) f. *How adequate are the facilities and opportunities for independent work?*

COMMENTS

IV. Direction of Learning

A. INSTRUCTIONAL STAFF

CHECKLIST

All teachers of science:

(   )   1. have a liberal education.

(   )   2. have preparation in physical sciences.

(   )   3. have preparation in biological science.

(   )   4. have an understanding of individual differences among students.

(   )   5. have knowledge of modern methods of teaching science.

(   )   6. are familiar with valuable community resources in science teaching.

(   )   7. participate in in-service education.

(   )   8. participate in science educational organizations.

(   )   9.

(   )   10.

EVALUATIONS

(   )   *a. How adequate is the preparation of the teachers in science?*

(   )   *b. How adequate is the preparation of teachers in the science methodology?*

(   )   *c. To what extent do teachers of science keep informed of modern trends in science?*

(   )   *d. To what extent do teachers of science participate in science activities of the community?*

COMMENTS

B. INSTRUCTIONAL ACTIVITIES

CHECKLIST

(   ) 1. Instruction emphasizes discovery of scientific truths by students.

(   ) 2. Instruction is geared to students of all ability levels.

(   ) 3. Instruction stimulates interest and fosters active participation of students.

(   ) 4. Science resources of the community and environment are used.

(   ) 5. Emphasis is placed upon the development of problem-solving techniques.

(   ) 6. Instruction includes correlation of science with other fields of learning.

(   ) 7. Use is made of multi-sensory aids, exhibits and projects, demonstrations, and individual and group experiments.

(   ) 8. Use is made of the variety of scientific literature.

(   ) 9. Use is made of competitive science events to a reasonable extent.

(   ) 10. Opportunities for advanced instruction are presented to gifted students.

(   ) 11.

(   ) 12.

EVALUATIONS

(   ) *a. How adequately do instructional activities provide for the need of the individual?*

(   ) *b. How adequately does the instruction provide for the need of the group?*

(   ) *c. How adequately do the teachers plan and prepare their work?*

(   ) *d. How adequately do instructional activities promote the use of the methods of science in problem-solving situations?*

(   ) *e. To what extent are the students challenged to do research?*

COMMENTS

C. INSTRUCTIONAL MATERIALS

CHECKLIST

The instructional materials for science include:

(   ) 1. equipment and supplies which are available for classroom demonstrations.

(   ) 2. equipment and supplies for individual and group laboratory work and projects.

(   ) 3. variety of books, periodicals, pamphlets, and reference materials appropriate for students of differing abilities and interests.

(   ) 4. variety of multi-sensory materials and equipment.

(   ) 5.

(   ) 6.

EVALUATIONS

(   ) *a. How adequate is the quality of instructional materials?*

(   ) *b. How adequate is the quantity of instructional materials?*

(   ) *c. How extensive is the variety of instructional materials?*

(   ) *d. To what extent are instructional materials organized?*

COMMENTS

D. METHODS OF EVALUATION

CHECKLIST

(   ) 1. Evaluation is an integral part of instruction.

(   ) 2. Evaluation is made by standardized tests and teacher-made tests of both objective and essay types.

(   ) 3. Evaluation provides for varying science abilities.

(   ) 4. Evaluation is made of the laboratory experiences of students.

(   ) 5. Evaluation is made of science projects of students.

(   ) 6. Evaluation is made of student demonstrations, experiments and reports.

(   ) 7. Evaluation includes student self-evaluation.

(   ) 8.

(   ) 9.

EVALUATIONS

(   ) *a. How effective are the evaluation procedures pertaining to the accepted objectives of science education?*

(   ) *b. How effectively do teachers use evaluation results?*

(   ) *c. To what extent does the evaluation identify individual abilities of students in science?*

(   ) *d. To what extent do students participate in self-evaluation?*

COMMENTS

V. Outcomes

EVALUATIONS

To what degree do students:

( ) a. *prove that they understand the basic principles of science?*

( ) b. *acquire a proper understanding of their relationship to God and their fellow man, self and nature?*

( ) c. *develop general scientific attitudes, skills, knowledge, understandings, and appreciations?*

( ) d. *demonstrate their abilities in experimentation and discovery?*

( ) e. *exhibit ability to apply the methods and techniques of science in problem solving?*

( ) f. *read and interpret scientific literature?*

( ) g. *recognize the truth or falsity of scientific claims in advertising and other related fields?*

( ) h. *pursue scientific interests in leisure activities?*

( ) i. *become acquainted with vocational opportunities in scientific fields?*

( ) j. *show an inclination to continue in the field of science in the secondary schools?*

VI. Special Characteristics of Science

1. What phases of science education fulfill the functions of the elementary school most satisfactorily?

 a.

 b.

 c.

 d.

2. What phases of science education need improvement?

 a.

 b.

 c.

 d.

VII. General Evaluation of Instruction in Science

EVALUATIONS

( ) a. *To what extent does instruction in science conform to the philosophy, objectives, and functions given in Section B?*

( ) b. *To what extent does instruction in science provide for the needs of students as given in Section C?*

( ) c. *To what extent does the school recognize problems in science instruction and seek their solution?*

Formulated and Edited by the Criteria Committee, Elementary School
Department of The National Catholic Educational Association

Student Activity Program

GUIDING PRINCIPLES

The student activity program is structured to meet the religious, intellectual, social, emotional, and physical needs of the students according to their age level and sex. It is coordinated with the offerings of community agencies.

A proper balance is maintained in the activity program which is designed to provide for large and small group activities. Intensively competitive activities are avoided and time and expenditure are in proportion to the overall educational program. Flexibility, informality, and democratic practices characterize the activity program. Initiative, creativity, student planning, and opportunity to develop leadership are encouraged under the direction of the staff.

Through periodic evaluation, the school staff determines the effectiveness of the student activity program in contributing to the personal development of every student.

NAME OF SCHOOL_____ DATE_____

ADDRESS_____

(ARCH)DIOCESE OF_____

SELF-EVALUATION MEMBERS_____

_____

_____

Instructions

When undertaking a self-evaluation the members of the school staff should use the statement of GUIDING PRINCIPLES and CHECKLIST items as an aid to determining the extent to which their school program coincides with the Philosophy and Objectives of the school and meets the needs of the school population and community served. Of necessity a staff will modify statements of Guiding Principles, Checklist items and Evaluations to conform with the philosophy and characteristics of the particular school doing the evaluation. Wherever changes are made the school should explain under Comments the reasons for the change in relation to its own program. Minor differences in terminology should not be regarded as significant items of change.

CHECKLISTS

Checklist items consist of statements deemed applicable to the area of the Criteria being evaluated. These are suggested ideas and are not to be interpreted as the only statements applicable to the area or as all-inclusive. A school may wish to add additional statements of its own that will explain further the particular program of the school. Space is provided in each Checklist for such additions. If the change is regarded as significant, the school will use the letter C in the Checklist as indicated in the following instructions and explain under Comments the precise nature of its offerings.

A staff should note that a definite relation pertains between Checklist items and Evaluations. Members of the staff should familiarize themselves with the definite meanings of Checklist symbols and Evaluation ratings.

CHECKLIST items may be indicated as follows:

E—The statement or condition is *extensive* in application.

M—The statement or condition is *moderately* achieved.

L—The statement or condition is *limited* in application.

MN—The condition is missing but judged needed by the staff.

N—The condition does not apply to this school.

*C—The condition is achieved in a manner different from Checklist items.

     * Wherever C is used, this aim should be stated in one of the additional numbers of the Checklist and explained under COMMENTS.

EVALUATIONS

Evaluations represent numerical summations of the Checklist items. The rating is determined from discussions of the staff as related to the consistency of the school program with stated Philosophy and Objectives.

To secure a composite view of the school's outcomes in each area of the Criteria, a school will project the Evaluation ratings to the X Blank of the respective areas. A further picture of the total program will be secured by tabulating the Average of the X Blank on the Graphic Summary provided in the Y Blank. Instructions for such procedure are listed in the X and Y Blanks.

Evaluations are indicated as follows:

5—The condition is excellent and extensive. (Please note that 5 does not mean "perfect.")

4—The condition is very good. A school may care to use a further refinement of 4a or 4b: 4a indicates that the condition is extensive and functioning well; 4b indicates that the condition is moderately extensive but functioning excellently.

3—The condition meets student needs to a reasonable degree.

2—The condition is in need of *achievable* improvement.

1—The condition is not being achieved and its need is not recognized.

*MN—The condition is missing but needed.

*N—The condition does not apply.

     * When MN or N are accepted by the staff for an *Evaluation* rating the divisor on the X Blank must be adjusted accordingly. N should not be used in CHECKLISTS and EVALUATIONS unless the condition absolutely DOES NOT APPLY. If the item is educationally desirable the school should not use N simply because it does not make use of the item. An adequate replacement for the item may fulfill the conditions of the Checklist.

I. General Organization and Nature

A. GENERAL ORGANIZATION OF THE PROGRAM

CHECKLIST

(   ) 1. The program is organized cooperatively by the administration and staff to meet the needs of elementary school students.

(   ) 2. Students participate in the planning of activities.

(   ) 3. Parents are consulted in organizing pertinent areas of the program.

(   ) 4. Community resources are considered and utilized in the organization of activities.

(   ) 5. Policy determination is in the hands of the school administration.

(   ) 6. Time allotted to activities is in proportion to needs of the program.

(   ) 7. A calendar of activities indicates the regular time and place of meetings.

(   ) 8. The need of students to assume responsibility in the activity program is provided for in the organizational plan.

(   ) 9. Student activities are properly supervised.

(   ) 10. The program is articulated with community activities.

(   ) 11. Records are kept of student participation in activities.

(   ) 12. All activity funds are handled by a bonded individual.

(   ) 13. The activity program is evaluated periodically by staff.

(   ) 14.

(   ) 15.

EVALUATIONS

(   ) *a. To what extent is cooperative planning used in the organization of the elementary school activity program?*

(   ) *b. To what extent is a proper balance maintained in the activity program?*

(   ) *c. To what extent does the student activity program develop leadership and responsibility?*

(   ) *d. To what extent are funds handled by a bonded individual?*

COMMENTS

B. GENERAL NATURE OF THE PROGRAM

CHECKLIST

(   ) 1. Activities are designed to meet religious, intellectual, emotional, social and physical needs of students.

(   ) 2. Varied activities suitable to age and sex of students are provided.

(   ) 3. The activity program provides opportunity to develop initiative and creativity.

(   ) 4. The activity program is planned to develop leadership and responsibility.

(   ) 5. The program provides opportunity to function within a democratic framework.

(   ) 6. Activities which teach a proper use of leisure time are included in the program.

(   ) 7.

(   ) 8.

EVALUATIONS

(   ) a. To what extent does the student activity program meet the needs of students?

(   ) b. To what extent does the activity program provide opportunity for the development of initiative and creativity?

(   ) c. To what extent does the activity program provide for leadership and responsibility?

COMMENTS

II. Service Activities

CHECKLIST

Students are given opportunity for religious development through activities such as:

(   )   1. liturgical worship.
(   )   2. religious societies.
(   )   3. mission education.
(   )   4. spiritual works of mercy.
(   )   5. corporal works of mercy.
(   )   6.
(   )   7.

Students are given opportunity to be of service to others through activities such as:

(   )   8. patrol system.
(   )   9. civics club.
(   ) 10. student council.
(   ) 11. volunteer work in community agencies.
(   ) 12. parish organizations.
(   ) 13.
(   ) 14.

SUPPLEMENTARY DATA *(Attach typed sheet)*

1. List types of religious activities and number of students participating.
2. List types of service activities and number of students participating.

EVALUATIONS

(   ) *a. To what extent is evidence given of voluntary participation in religious activities?*
(   ) *b. To what extent is evidence given of voluntary participation in service activities?*

COMMENTS

III. Creative Activities

CHECKLIST

Adequate opportunity is given for self-expression through activities such as:

( ) 1. discussions.
( ) 2. reports.
( ) 3. choral speaking.
( ) 4. dramatizations.

( ) 5.

( ) 6.

Offerings in music and art provide for varying abilities and levels through activities such as:

( ) 7. liturgical music.
( ) 8. choral groups.
( ) 9. dancing.
( ) 10. band and/or orchestra.
( ) 11. operas, concerts, etc.
( ) 12. art displays.

( ) 13.

( ) 14.

Creative abilities of students are developed through communications such as:

( ) 15. class newspapers.
( ) 16. school newspapers.
( ) 17. bulletin board displays.
( ) 18. school assemblies.
( ) 19. letters to benefactors, of condolence, etc.

( ) 20.

( ) 21.

Creative abilities of students are developed through general activities such as:

( ) 22. science fairs.
( ) 23. field trips.
( ) 24. demonstrations for home-school meetings.

( ) 25.

( ) 26.

SUPPLEMENTARY DATA *(Attach typed sheet)*

1. List activities of drama and speech and number of participants in each area.
2. List activities of music and art and number of participants in each area.
3. List communication activities and number of participants in each area.
4. List general activities and the number of participants in each area.

EVALUATIONS

( ) *a. How adequately do drama and speech activities meet the needs of students?*
( ) *b. How adequately do the music and art activities meet the needs of students?*
( ) *c. How adequately do communication activities meet the needs of students?*
( ) *d. How adequately do general activities meet the needs of students?*

COMMENTS

IV. Physical Activities

CHECKLIST (*Check each item as it applies to boys and to girls*)

B   G

( ) ( ) 1. Physical activities are determined according to the needs and interests of the students.

( ) ( ) 2. A major emphasis is given to those games, sports, or activities which have value for leisure time.

( ) ( ) 3. A varied program of team and intramural physical activities is provided.

( ) ( ) 4. Activities which place undue stress on competition are excluded from the program.

( ) ( ) 5. Students engaging in physical activities pass a physical examination by a qualified physician.

( ) ( ) 6. Students engaging in physical activities are insured.

B   G

( ) ( ) 7. Provision is made for interscholastic physical activities.

( ) ( ) 8. Students engaging in interscholastic activities have written approval from parents.

( ) ( ) 9. Eligibility standards regulating participation in interscholastic competition are in writing and are maintained.

( ) ( ) 10. Courtesy to officials and members of teams is shown by participants and spectators.

( ) ( ) 11.

( ) ( ) 12.

SUPPLEMENTARY DATA (*Attach typed sheet*)

1. Include list of intramural activities, age and sex of participants and the number of students participating.
2. Include list of interscholastic activities, age and sex of participants, and number of students participating.

EVALUATIONS

B   G

( ) ( ) *a. To what extent does the school maintain control over all physical activities?*

( ) ( ) *b. To what extent are intramural physical activities appropriate for students of elementary school age?*

( ) ( ) *c. To what extent are interscholastic physical activities appropriate for students of elementary school age?*

( ) ( ) *d. To what extent are the health and safety of participants maintained?*

( ) ( ) *e. To what extent is the emotional health of participants promoted?*

( ) ( ) *f. To what extent do physical activities contribute to good sportsmanship?*

COMMENTS

V. Special Characteristics of Student Activity Program

1. What are the most commendable features of the student activity program?

a.

b.

c.

d.

2. In what areas is the activity program in need of improvement?

a.

b.

c.

d.

VI. General Evaluation of the Student Activity Program

EVALUATIONS

(   ) *a. To what extent does the program meet the objectives set forth in Section B?*

(   ) *b. To what extent does the program meet student needs as outlined in Section C?*

(   ) *c. How effectively is the school improving unsatisfactory conditions noted in the activity program?*

CRITERIA FOR EVALUATION
OF
CATHOLIC ELEMENTARY SCHOOLS, 1965

F

Formulated and Edited by the Criteria Committee, Elementary School
Department of The National Catholic Educational Association

Instructional Materials Services
—Library and Multi-Sensory Aids

GUIDING PRINCIPLES

The elementary school library should offer both the challenge and possibility of attaining the educational objectives emanating from the philosophy of the school. The central library offers a wide range of resources, many special services and experiences important to students, and opportunities to learn how to use a library effectively. The goal of the library program is to stimulate student growth in factual knowledge, critical reading and thinking, literary and aesthetic appreciation, choice of genuine values, and acceptance of ethical standards.

The school library serves as a center for instructional materials. The term, instructional materials center, means a collection of print and nonprint materials and equipment selected and organized by a competent staff and so located as to help faculty and students achieve the objectives of the school.

The criteria which follow are intended for an evaluation of administration, organization, specifications for staff, funds, quarters, materials collections, and equipment needed in an instructional materials center.

In addition to the instructional materials center, classroom collections supplied with currently interesting materials for curriculum enrichment lure students to browse or read; however, classroom collections do not serve as a substitute for an instructional materials center. The classroom collection and the instructional materials center are inseparable and essential in fostering quality education.

NAME OF SCHOOL_____ DATE_____

ADDRESS_____

(ARCH)DIOCESE OF_____

SELF-EVALUATION MEMBERS_____

_____

_____

145

Instructions

When undertaking a self-evaluation the members of the school staff should use the statement of GUIDING PRINCIPLES and CHECKLIST items as an aid to determining the extent to which their school program coincides with the Philosophy and Objectives of the school and meets the needs of the school population and community served. Of necessity a staff will modify statements of Guiding Principles, Checklist items and Evaluations to conform with the philosophy and characteristics of the particular school doing the evaluation. Wherever changes are made the school should explain under Comments the reasons for the change in relation to its own program. Minor differences in terminology should not be regarded as significant items of change.

CHECKLISTS

Checklist items consist of statements deemed applicable to the area of the Criteria being evaluated. These are suggested ideas and are not to be interpreted as the only statements applicable to the area or as all-inclusive. A school may wish to add additional statements of its own that will explain further the particular program of the school. Space is provided in each Checklist for such additions. If the change is regarded as significant, the school will use the letter C in the Checklist as indicated in the following instructions and explain under Comments the precise nature of its offerings.

A staff should note that a definite relation pertains between Checklist items and Evaluations. Members of the staff should familiarize themselves with the definite meanings of Checklist symbols and Evaluation ratings.

CHECKLIST items may be indicated as follows:

E—The statement or condition is *extensive* in application.

M—The statement or condition is *moderately* achieved.

L—The statement or condition is limited in application.

MN—The condition is missing but judged needed by the staff.

N—The condition does not apply to this school.

*C—The condition is achieved in a manner different from Checklist items.

  * Wherever C is used, this aim should be stated in one of the additional numbers of the Checklist and explained under COMMENTS.

EVALUATIONS

Evaluations represent numerical summations of the Checklist items. The rating is determined from discussions of the staff as related to the consistency of the school program with stated Philosophy and Objectives.

To secure a composite view of the school's outcomes in each area of the Criteria, a school will project the Evaluation ratings to the X Blank of the respective areas. A further picture of the total program will be secured by tabulating the Average of the X Blank on the Graphic Summary provided in the Y Blank. Instructions for such procedure are listed in the X and Y Blanks.

Evaluations are indicated as follows:

5—The condition is excellent and extensive. (Please note that 5 does not mean "perfect.")

4—The condition is very good. A school may care to use a further refinement of 4a or 4b: 4a indicates that the condition is extensive and functioning well; 4b indicates that the condition is moderately extensive but functioning excellently.

3—The condition meets student needs to a reasonable degree.

2—The condition is in need of *achievable* improvement.

1—The condition is not being achieved and its need is not recognized.

*MN—The condition is missing but needed.

 *N—The condition does not apply.

  * When MN or N are accepted by the staff for an *Evaluation* rating the divisor on the X Blank must be adjusted accordingly. N should not be used in CHECKLISTS and EVALUATIONS unless the condition absolutely DOES NOT APPLY. If the item is educationally desirable the school should not use N simply because it does not make use of the item. An adequate replacement for the item may fulfill the conditions of the Checklist.

I. Instructional Materials Staff (Library and Multi-Sensory Aids)

A. NUMERICAL ADEQUACY

CHECKLIST

(   ) 1. An adequately prepared staff is in charge of the instructional materials center.

(   ) 2. Paid clerical service is adequate.

(   ) 3. Competent volunteer help is provided.

(   ) 4. Student aides are taught to serve as library assistants.

(   ) 5. Student aides are taught to assist in the operation of multi-sensory equipment.

(   ) 6.

(   ) 7.

SUPPLEMENTARY DATA

1. Number of professional librarians.._____

2. Number of part-time librarians.._____

3. Number of paid clerical assistants.._____

4. Number of hours per week given by teachers to instructional materials duty ...._____

5. Number of hours per week given by adult volunteer help ...._____

6. Number of student assistants..._____

7. Number of hours per week provided by student help..._____

8. Number of outside consultants, e.g., state school library supervisor, public library personnel......_____

EVALUATIONS

(   ) *a. How adequate is the staff personnel of the instructional materials center to meet needs of the school?*

(   ) *b. How adequate is paid clerical help?*

(   ) *c. How adequate is service given by teachers to the instructional materials center?*

(   ) *d. How adequate is volunteer service?*

(   ) *e. How adequate is student-assistants service?*

(   ) *f. How adequate is assistance from outside consultants?*

COMMENTS

B. GENERAL QUALIFICATIONS

CHECKLIST

Staff members of the instructional materials center:

( ) 1. have an understanding of the philosophy and educational objectives of the school.

( ) 2. have a knowledge of curriculum.

( ) 3. have skill in instruction techniques.

( ) 4. have specialized knowledge in instructional materials service.

( ) 5. have certification in library science.

( ) 6. have adequate preparation in audio-visual education.

( ) 7. have a sympathetic understanding of children and childhood.

( ) 8. have the ability, tact, and enthusiasm to make school life challenging.

( ) 9. have an intimate acquaintance with children's literature.

( ) 10. have critical acumen to recognize literary merit and educational value in books and other instructional materials.

( ) 11. are alert to new developments in elementary education.

( ) 12.

( ) 13.

EVALUATIONS

( ) *a. How adequate are general qualifications of staff members of the instructional materials center?*
( ) *b. How aware are staff members of child growth and development?*
( ) *c. How alert is the professional staff to new educational developments?*
( ) *d. How conversant are staff members with new materials in various instructional areas?*

COMMENTS

C. RESPONSIBILITIES

CHECKLIST

Staff members of instructional materials center:

( ) 1. work closely with faculty in planning an integrated, sequential program suited to needs of students.

( ) 2. work closely with faculty in making the instructional materials center of maximum service.

( ) 3. share school's responsibility for teaching students to use intelligently the instructional materials center.

( ) 4. select and purchase, under faculty advisement, instructional materials and equipment.

( ) 5. endeavor to meet faculty needs in professional areas.

( ) 6. maintain good operational relations with the public library through conferences, visits, and reports.

( ) 7. acquaint parents with services of the instructional materials center.

( ) 8. keep school administrators and parents informed of needs of the instructional materials center.

( ) 9. work to promote effective articulation of the instructional materials center with the secondary school.

( ) 10. take inventories of the instructional materials.

( ) 11. keep abreast of research and publications in the instructional materials field.

( ) 12. attend local, state and national school library meetings.

( ) 13.

( ) 14.

EVALUATIONS

( ) *a. How effectively do instructional materials staff members fulfill their responsibilities to students?*
( ) *b. How effectively do instructional materials staff members fulfill their responsibilities to faculty?*
( ) *c. How effectively do instructional materials staff members keep parents aware of services and needs of the center?*
( ) *d. To what extent are staff members alert to research and recent trends in library science?*

COMMENTS

D. SERVICES

1. Services for Faculty and Administrators

CHECKLIST

Members of the instructional materials center staff:

(   ) 1. keep faculty informed about the constantly growing basic professional book collection.

(   ) 2. provide professional magazines.

(   ) 3. strive to make the instructional materials center of maximum service to the faculty.

(   ) 4. share with faculty all library aids, e.g., indexes and bibliographies of instructional materials.

(   ) 5. keep school staff informed of new acquisitions through library bulletins.

(   ) 6. aid faculty in planning for effective classroom use of materials and equipment.

(   ) 7. help faculty prepare exhibits and display areas.

(   ) 8. work with faculty in stimulating students to frequent and effective use of instructional materials.

(   ) 9. observe students in the instructional materials center for purpose of sharing with faculty information about reading interests, needs, habits of study and reading behavior.

(   ) 10. send collections to classrooms for short-term loans ranging from a class period to several weeks.

(   ) 11. send collections to classrooms for long-term loans.

(   ) 12.

(   ) 13.

CHECKLIST

Members of the instructional materials center staff:

(   ) 1. provide an effective reading guidance program.

(   ) 2. help satisfy individual reading needs.

(   ) 3. foster discriminating attitudes toward selection of reading materials.

(   ) 4. develop an appreciation of good literature.

(   ) 5. develop pride in personal ownership of books.

(   ) 6. provide continuous, sequential growth in library skills.

(   ) 7. help improve listening and viewing skills of students.

(   ) 8. offer enrichment in all phases of the school program.

(   ) 9. develop research skills and independent reading.

(   ) 10. inculcate habit of using the instructional materials center.

(   ) 11. make the instructional materials center contribute to personal, social, and ethical growth of students.

(   ) 12.

(   ) 13.

SUPPLEMENTARY DATA

1. Average daily attendance (number of students) using the instructional materials center.........._____

2. Average daily circulation of books..._____

EVALUATIONS

(   ) *a. How effectively do faculty and instructional materials staff work together?*

(   ) *b. How well informed are administrators and faculty about services and needs of the instructional materials center?*

(   ) *c. How effectively does the instructional materials staff work with students?*

(   ) *d. How up-to-date and complete are evaluation records?*

COMMENTS

II. Organization and Management

A. FINANCIAL PROVISIONS

CHECKLIST

(   ) 1. A sum of money is allotted annually for purchase of new books.

(   ) 2. A sum of money is allotted annually for purchase of magazines, newspapers, pamphlets, encyclopedias, and other reference aids.

(   ) 3. A sum of money is allotted annually for bindings and supplies.

(   ) 4. A sum of money is allotted annually for multi-sensory materials and equipment.

(   ) 5.

(   ) 6.

SUPPLEMENTARY DATA

Enter expenditures for the past three-year period:

	EXPENDITURES	
Year ___	Year ___	Year ___
Books			
Magazines			
Newspapers			
Pamphlets			
Multi-sensory equipment			
Multi-sensory instructional materials purchased...			
Multi-sensory instructional materials rented......			
Encyclopedias, dictionaries			
Supplies			
Bindings			
Professional literature			
Memberships			
Professional travel			
Totals			

EVALUATIONS

(   ) a. *How sufficient are funds for purchase of books?*

(   ) b. *How sufficient are funds for purchase of other printed materials?*

(   ) c. *How sufficient are funds for purchase of multi-sensory materials and equipment?*

(   ) d. *How sufficient are funds for supplies and repair of books?*

COMMENTS

B. SELECTION OF MATERIALS AND EQUIPMENT

CHECKLIST

(   )   1. Systematically developed book collections are well-balanced.

(   )   2. Multi-sensory collections are representative of quantitative and qualitative standards.

(   )   3. Collections are continually reevaluated in terms of changing curriculum content, new techniques of teaching and current needs of teachers and standards.

(   )   4. Community resources, e.g., individuals in the community, public library, parish library, museums, mobile units are inventoried.

(   )   5. Materials are selected with consideration of teachers' requests and student suggestions.

(   )   6. Final approval of purchase of new materials and equipment rests with principal and librarian in charge of the materials center.

(   )   7. Materials and equipment are purchased as needed throughout the school year.

(   )   8. Well-established criteria for evaluation and selection of instructional materials and equipment are worked out cooperatively and recorded.

Criteria for the selection of instructional materials and equipment include:

(   )   9. philosophy, educational objectives and curriculum of the school.

(   ) 10. varied range of abilities, needs, interests and maturity levels of student body.

(   ) 11. opinion of experts in use of instructional materials and equipment.

(   ) 12.

(   ) 13.

EVALUATIONS

(   ) a. *How sufficient are means for selection of instructional materials and equipment?*

(   ) b. *How adequate are provisions for evaluation and selection of materials and equipment in terms of philosophy, educational objectives, and curriculum of school?*

(   ) c. *How adequate is involvement of faculty in selection and evaluation of instructional materials and equipment?*

(   ) d. *How extensively is the opinion of specialists sought?*

COMMENTS

C. CLASSIFYING, CATALOGING, AND PROCESSING OF MATERIALS

CHECKLIST

(　) 1. Materials are organized to permit efficient service to teachers and students.

(　) 2. Book collection is cataloged and classified according to standard elementary school procedures.

(　) 3. Multi-sensory materials are cataloged and arranged according to standard procedure.

(　) 4. Books and multi-sensory materials housed in classrooms are accessioned, classified and cataloged centrally.

(　) 5. Magazines, newspapers, and pamphlets are organized and arranged for quick, effective use.

(　) 6. Print and nonprint materials are indexed in card catalog under author, title and subject.

(　) 7. The instructional materials center maintains simple records for acquisition of materials and equipment.

(　) 8.

(　) 9.

EVALUATIONS

(　) a. *How adequate for effective service is organization of books?*

(　) b. *How adequate for prompt, effective use is arrangement of magazines, newspapers, and pamphlets?*

(　) c. *How adequate for maximum service is the organization of multi-sensory materials and equipment?*

(　) d. *How accurate, complete and up-to-date is the card catalog?*

(　) e. *How informative and up-to-date are acquisition records?*

COMMENTS

D. ACCESSIBILITY OF INSTRUCTIONAL MATERIALS SERVICES

CHECKLIST

( ) 1. The materials center is easily accessible.

( ) 2. The materials center is open to teachers and students before the beginning of class.

( ) 3. The materials center is open to teachers and students continuously throughout the school day.

( ) 4. The materials center is open to teachers and students for use after close of school day.

( ) 5. Books may be selected for home use.

( ) 6. Multi-sensory materials and equipment are accessible for use in the materials center or for prompt delivery to classrooms.

( ) 7.

( ) 8.

EVALUATIONS

( ) *a. How accessible are print and nonprint instructional materials for effective use?*

( ) *b. How accessible are multi-sensory instructional materials and equipment?*

COMMENTS

E. CARE AND MAINTENANCE OF MATERIALS AND EQUIPMENT

CHECKLIST

( ) 1. Books are properly shelved.

( ) 2. Magazines, pamphlets and pictures are properly filed for maximum use.

( ) 3. Multi-sensory materials and equipment are regularly examined and repaired if needed.

( ) 4. Books and pamphlets are rebound or repaired when necessary.

( ) 5.

( ) 6.

EVALUATIONS

( ) *a. To what extent are provisions made for care and maintenance of instructional materials?*

( ) *b. To what extent are provisions made for care and maintenance of multi-sensory equipment?*

COMMENTS

III. Materials

A. PRINTED MATERIALS

1. Books *(Fill in requested numerical data and evaluation)*

CLASSIFICATION	NUMBER OF DIFFERENT TITLES	NUMBER OF VOLUMES	NUMBER OF TITLES COPYRIGHTED WITHIN PAST FIVE YEARS	EVALUATION: HOW EFFECTIVELY DOES EACH MAJOR CLASSIFICATION MEET SCHOOL NEEDS?
000 General Works: encyclopedias, atlases				a) ( )
100 Philosophy: books which tell us how to think, act, live				b) ( )
200 Religion: Bible and books which tell how people worship				c) ( )
300 Social Science: books on law, government, education, etiquette, how to get along with people, fairy tales				d) ( )
400 Language: spellers, grammars, dictionaries				e) ( )
500 Science: books about stars, animals, plants, space, mathematics				f) ( )
600 Useful Arts: books which tell us how to make and do useful things, cookery, aviation				g) ( )
700 Fine Arts: books about music, painting, sculpture, sports, games				h) ( )
800 Literature: books of poetry, plays, essays				i) ( )
900 History: books about travel, geography				j) ( )
92–920 Biography: lives of individuals and groups of individuals				k) ( )
F– FICTION				l) ( )
E– Easy Books: picture books				m) ( )
TOTAL				

COMMENTS

III. Materials

A. PRINTED MATERIALS

2. Periodicals and Newspapers

CHECKLIST

(　) 1. Periodicals and newspapers are supplied to keep teachers and students aware of national and international events.

(　) 2. Periodicals designed to meet the interests and needs of primary students are supplied.

(　) 3. Periodicals designed to meet the interests and needs of intermediate grade students are supplied.

(　) 4. Periodicals designed to meet the interests and needs of upper grade students are supplied.

(　) 5. Diocesan newspapers and pamphlets are available.

(　) 6. Professional magazines are supplied to meet needs of faculty.

(　) 7. Periodicals are supplied which are of current interest in all areas of the curriculum.

(　) 8. Attention is given to reading interests of boys.

(　) 9. Attention is given to reading interests of girls.

(　) 10.

(　) 11.

EVALUATIONS

(　) *a. To what extent do periodicals meet teacher needs?*

(　) *b. To what extent do periodicals meet student needs?*

COMMENTS

III. Materials

A. PRINTED MATERIALS

3. Vertical File Materials and Pamphlets.

CHECKLIST

( ) 1. A current index of community resources, field trips and lecture files, materials on local history, and vocational information services is available to students and teachers.

( ) 2. Vertical files consist of pictures and pamphlets; important pamphlets are processed.

( ) 3. Vertical files material is examined periodically and kept up-to-date.

( ) 4.

( ) 5.

( ) 6.

EVALUATIONS

( ) *a. How current are various indexes of available materials?*

( ) *b. How adequate is the picture collection?*

( ) *c. How readily available for student use are vertical file materials?*

COMMENTS

B. NONPRINT MATERIALS

TYPE OF MATERIAL	NUMBER OF TITLES OWNED BY SCHOOL	NUMBER OF TITLES RENTED OR BORROWED FROM OTHER SOURCES DURING THE MOST RECENT YEAR	NUMBER OF TITLES BORROWED FROM SCHOOL SYSTEM CENTRAL DEPOSITORY DURING THE MOST RECENT YEAR	EVALUATION: HOW ADEQUATE ARE THE RESOURCES IN MULTI-SENSORY MATERIALS?
Films				a ( )
Filmstrips				b ( )
Slides				c ( )
Records				d ( )
Tape recordings				e ( )
Pictures				f ( )
Maps, charts				g ( )
Realia: dioramas				h ( )
models				i ( )
museum materials				j ( )
Others (list)				k ( )

IV. Physical Facilities

A. QUARTERS

CHECKLIST

( ) 1. The location of the materials center offers accessibility and quiet.

( ) 2. Adequate space is provided for housing and convenient arrangement of materials and equipment.

( ) 3. There is proper control of lighting, temperature, ventilation, and acoustics.

( ) 4. Work areas for technical processing and repairing of materials are adequate.

( ) 5. Work and storage areas open into the materials center and also into corridor.

( ) 6. Glass vision panels between librarian's office and materials center make supervision possible.

( ) 7. Separate space for collection of professional books and materials for faculty is provided.

( ) 8. Reading room provides space according to accepted standard.

( ) 9.

( ) 10.

EVALUATIONS

( ) *a. How accessible is the materials center?*

( ) *b. How adequate is the space allowed for the materials center?*

( ) *c. How adequate is the control of temperature, ventilation, lighting, and acoustics?*

( ) *d. How flexible are materials center quarters for new developments in educational programs, teaching techniques, and class grouping?*

COMMENTS

IV. Physical Facilities

B. FURNISHINGS AND FIXED EQUIPMENT

CHECKLIST

The instructional materials center (reading room, workroom) is provided with:

(   ) 1. standard adjustable shelving of sufficient quantity.

(   ) 2. specific shelving for:
> picture books.
> records.
> tape recordings.
> magazines.
> newspapers.

(   ) 3. dictionary stands.

(   ) 4. atlas stands.

(   ) 5. circulation desk with filing trays, book cards, and a section for returned books.

(   ) 6. card catalog cabinets.

(   ) 7. book trucks.

(   ) 8. legal size filing cabinets.

(   ) 9. typewriters.

(   ) 10. office desk.

(   ) 11. glass exhibit cases.

(   ) 12. cork and peg boards.

(   ) 13. sink with hot and cold running water.

(   ) 14. stools (sitting and step).

(   ) 15. tables and chairs of suitable sizes.

(   ) 16. attractive furnishings reflecting beauty and providing comfort.

(   ) 17.

(   ) 18.

EVALUATIONS

(   ) a. *To what extent are furnishings and equipment adequate?*

(   ) b. *To what extent do furnishings and equipment make the instructional materials center a pleasant and inviting place?*

COMMENTS

IV. Physical Facilities

C. MULTI-SENSORY EQUIPMENT AND FACILITIES

CHECKLIST

1. Multi-sensory equipment and facilities are provided: (Insert number below)

    (   ) 8-16 mm. sound projectors _____

    (   ) filmstrip and 2 x 2 projectors _____

    (   ) radios _____

    (   ) television sets _____

    (   ) opaque projectors _____

    (   ) overhead projectors _____

    (   ) individual viewers _____

    (   ) record players _____

    (   ) tape recorders _____

    (   ) projection screens:

            wall _____

            portable _____

2. (   ) equipment for instruction by television _____

3. (   ) mechanical copying machines _____

4. (   )

5. (   )

EVALUATIONS

(   ) *a. How extensive is multi-sensory equipment?*

(   ) *b. How extensive is the maintenance of the multi-sensory equipment?*

(   ) *c. How extensive are the physical facilities for multi-sensory equipment?*

COMMENTS

V. Special Characteristics of Instructional Materials Services

1. What are the outstanding characteristics of the instructional materials services?

   a.

   b.

   c.

2. What are the chief weaknesses of the instructional materials services?

   a.

   b.

   c.

3. What improvements in the instructional materials services have been made during the past three years?

   a.

   b.

   c.

4. What further improvements are being considered or are presently under way?

   a.

   b.

   c.

VI. General Evaluations of Instructional Materials Services

EVALUATIONS

( ) *a. How well do the instructional materials services reflect the Christian philosophy of education as outlined in Section B?*

( ) *b. How strongly do the instructional materials services motivate faculty and students to attain the educational objectives as outlined in Section C?*

( ) *c. How adequately does the school make provision for the instructional materials to stimulate growth in factual knowledge, critical thinking, literary appreciation, aesthetic sense, and genuine standards?*

( ) *d. How effectively do the instructional materials services promote quality education?*

COMMENTS

Formulated and Edited by the Criteria Committee, Elementary School
Department of The National Catholic Educational Association

Guidance Services

GUIDING PRINCIPLES

Guidance is an integral part of the elementary school. It is organized by the administration to provide an adequate and well-coordinated program structured to help the student in achieving self-acceptance and self-direction. Assistance is given in solving religious, educational, vocational, social, and emotional problems.

Classroom teachers exercise a major role in the guidance program and work with parents in directing the student in the development of his potential. Psychologists, test experts and other specialized personnel are available for consultation and referral.

Pertinent information concerning each student is kept in a cumulative folder accessible to qualified personnel. Each member of the school staff has responsibility in the program and works cooperatively with guidance personnel.

NAME OF SCHOOL_____ DATE_____

ADDRESS_____

(ARCH)DIOCESE OF_____

SELF-EVALUATION MEMBERS_____

_____

_____

Instructions

When undertaking a self-evaluation the members of the school staff should use the statement of GUIDING PRINCIPLES and CHECKLIST items as an aid to determining the extent to which their school program coincides with the Philosophy and Objectives of the school and meets the needs of the school population and community served. Of necessity a staff will modify statements of Guiding Principles, Checklist items and Evaluations to conform with the philosophy and characteristics of the particular school doing the evaluation. Wherever changes are made the school should explain under Comments the reasons for the change in relation to its own program. Minor differences in terminology should not be regarded as significant items of change.

CHECKLISTS

Checklist items consist of statements deemed applicable to the area of the Criteria being evaluated. These are suggested ideas and are not to be interpreted as the only statements applicable to the area or as all-inclusive. A school may wish to add additional statements of its own that will explain further the particular program of the school. Space is provided in each Checklist for such additions. If the change is regarded as significant, the school will use the letter C in the Checklist as indicated in the following instructions and explain under Comments the precise nature of its offerings.

A staff should note that a definite relation pertains between Checklist items and Evaluations. Members of the staff should familiarize themselves with the definite meanings of Checklist symbols and Evaluation ratings.

CHECKLIST items may be indicated as follows:

E—The statement or condition is *extensive* in application.

M—The statement or condition is *moderately* achieved.

L—The statement or condition is *limited* in application.

MN—The condition is missing but judged needed by the staff.

N—The condition does not apply to this school.

*C—The condition is achieved in a manner different from Checklist items.

   * Wherever C is used, this aim should be stated in one of the additional numbers of the Checklist and explained under COMMENTS.

EVALUATIONS

Evaluations represent numerical summations of the Checklist items. The rating is determined from discussions of the staff as related to the consistency of the school program with stated Philosophy and Objectives.

To secure a composite view of the school's outcomes in each area of the Criteria, a school will project the Evaluation ratings to the X Blank of the respective areas. A further picture of the total program will be secured by tabulating the Average of the X Blank on the Graphic Summary provided in the Y Blank. Instructions for such procedure are listed in the X and Y Blanks.

Evaluations are indicated as follows:

5—The condition is excellent and extensive. (Please note that 5 does not mean "perfect.")

4—The condition is very good. A school may care to use a further refinement of 4a or 4b: 4a indicates that the condition is extensive and functioning well; 4b indicates that the condition is moderately extensive but functioning excellently.

3—The condition meets student needs to a reasonable degree.

2—The condition is in need of *achievable* improvement.

1—The condition is not being achieved and its need is not recognized.

*MN—The condition is missing but needed.

 *N—The condition does not apply.

   * When MN or N are accepted by the staff for an *Evaluation* rating the divisor on the X Blank must be adjusted accordingly. N should not be used in CHECKLISTS and EVALUATIONS unless the condition absolutely DOES NOT APPLY. If the item is educationally desirable the school should not use N simply because it does not make use of the item. An adequate replacement for the item may fulfill the conditions of the Checklist.

I. General Organization and Nature

CHECKLIST

(   ) 1. The responsibility for the organization of the guidance program rests with the administration and staff.

(   ) 2. The school personnel form the guidance staff.

(   ) 3. The classroom teacher plays the major role in the guidance program.

(   ) 4. Parents work cooperatively with the staff in guidance activities.

(   ) 5. Services of specialized guidance personnel are available for consultation and referrals.

(   ) 6. Guidance services are coordinated with programs of schools in the community.

(   ) 7. Community resources are utilized in the guidance program.

(   ) 8. Data are collected, organized, and made available for use in the guidance program.

(   ) 9. The guidance program provides assistance in solving problems of a religious, educational, physical, social and emotional nature.

(   ) 10. Guidance is preventive as well as adjustive.

(   ) 11. Guidance assists students in self-acceptance and self-direction.

(   ) 12. Guidance directs students to accept responsibility.

(   ) 13. Counseling is a part of the guidance program.

(   ) 14. The program provides for group and individual guidance.

(   ) 15. Revisions of guidance program are based on evaluation and research.

(   ) 16.

(   ) 17.

EVALUATIONS

(   ) *a. To what extent is the guidance program a cooperative project of the staff and community agencies.*

(   ) *b. To what extent is the guidance program structured to meet student needs?*

COMMENTS

II. Guidance Staff

PREPARATION AND QUALIFICATIONS

CHECKLIST

Teachers responsible for guidance have:

(   )   1. a code of professional ethics.

(   )   2. positive attitudes toward the guidance program.

(   )   3. personal qualities which lead to effective rapport.

(   )   4. a liberal education.

(   )   5. courses in psychology and mental health.

(   )   6. knowledge of basic principles of guidance.

(   )   7. ability in administration of tests and in interpretation of results.

(   )   8. ability to recognize behavior which requires services of specialists.

(   )   9. knowledge of professional services and referral agencies available to students.

(   )   10.

(   )   11.

EVALUATIONS

(   )   *a. To what extent are positive attitudes manifested toward the guidance program?*

(   )   *b. How satisfactory is the preparation of the teachers responsible for guidance?*

COMMENTS

III. Guidance Services

A. INFORMATION ABOUT STUDENTS

1. Sources of Information

Significant information is necessary for an effective guidance program. This is best obtained at the time of the student's entrance into the school, with additional information being added to records as the student progresses. Pertinent information is kept in a cumulative folder. It is complete, objective, easily interpreted, and regarded with professional secrecy.

CHECKLIST

Information includes the following entries:

( ) 1. statistical data, including the date of birth, date of entrance into school, age, photograph, etc.

( ) 2. information concerning home background, to include socio-economic status of family, religion, race, education of parents and siblings.

( ) 3. pre-school information, including any serious problems which originated during this period.

( ) 4. record of mental aptitude and special aptitudes.

( ) 5. school history of past education, including scholastic grades and record of attendance.

( ) 6. results of standardized achievement tests.

( ) 7. personal traits and attitudes.

( ) 8. health and physical growth.

( ) 9. anecdotal records.

( ) 10. sociometric studies.

( ) 11. observation of behavior.

( ) 12. case studies.

( ) 13. conferences.

( ) 14. participation in school activities.

( ) 15. home visits.

( ) 16.

( ) 17.

EVALUATIONS

( ) *a. How adequate is the compilation of data pertinent to the guidance program?*

( ) *b. How current are data on students?*

COMMENTS

2. Maintenance and Use of Information

CHECKLIST

( ) 1. Objective data are entered sequentially on cumulative records.

( ) 2. Entries are complete and accurate.

( ) 3. Graphs and charts are used to interpret test results.

( ) 4. Record forms facilitate duplication of data.

( ) 5. Clerical detail is kept at a minimum.

( ) 6. Data records are kept centrally located in a fireproof file.

( ) 7. Data records are accessible to qualified personnel.

( ) 8. Data records are utilized in guidance.

( ) 9.

( ) 10.

EVALUATIONS

( ) *a. To what extent are records accessible to qualified personnel?*

( ) *b. How adequate is the provision for storage of records?*

COMMENTS

B. GUIDANCE OF STUDENTS

CHECKLIST

(   ) 1. Teachers are available for group and individual guidance.

(   ) 2. Provision is made for individual counseling.

(   ) 3. Mutual confidence is reflected through teacher-student rapport.

(   ) 4. Guidance is concerned with all aspects of student growth and development.

(   ) 5. Guidance is determined by analysis of student behavior.

(   ) 6. Students are guided to formulate realistic goals.

(   ) 7. Students are provided with opportunities to make decisions and to develop a sense of responsibility.

(   ) 8. Specialized guidance personnel are used for consultation and referrals.

(   ) 9.

(   ) 10.

EVALUATIONS

(   ) *a. To what extent are teachers available for guidance?*

(   ) *b. How adequate are the guidance services offered?*

(   ) *c. How effective is the guidance program?*

COMMENTS

C. PLACEMENT SERVICES

CHECKLIST

(   ) 1. Provision is made for transfer of students within the school.

(   ) 2. Adequate reports, including academic and health records, are sent to schools when students transfer.

(   ) 3. Information is available concerning secondary school curricular offerings.

(   ) 4. Information is available concerning entrance requirements to high schools.

(   ) 5.

(   ) 6.

EVALUATIONS

(   ) *a. To what extent have adequate provisions been made to assist students who transfer?*

(   ) *b. To what extent is information available from secondary schools?*

COMMENTS

IV. Special Characteristics of the Guidance Service

1. What are the best characteristics of the guidance program?

    a.

    b.

    c.

    d.

    e.

2. What improvements would the staff like to make in the guidance program?

    a.

    b.

    c.

    d.

    e.

V. General Evaluation of Guidance Services

EVALUATIONS

(   ) a. *To what extent are guidance services consistent with the philosophy and objectives as outlined in Section B?*
(   ) b. *To what extent do guidance services meet the needs of students as described in Section C?*
(   ) c. *To what extent is the school analyzing its guidance services and seeking improvement?*

COMMENTS

Formulated and Edited by the Criteria Committee, Elementary School
Department of The National Catholic Educational Association

Health and Safety Services

GUIDING PRINCIPLES

School health and safety services are provided as part of the elementary school program in order to insure a sound physical basis for the spiritual, intellectual, emotional, and social growth of each student. Although such services will vary according to state legislation, the wide diversity of school population, available facilities, administrative regulations, and allocated personnel, all are designed to assist in protecting and improving student health and safety. Major functions include: periodic appraisal and follow-up of students' health status; parental, student and staff counseling in health and safety measures; encouraging students to take advantage of available treatment for the adjustment of remediable defects; discovering and educating exceptional children; observing signs or symptoms of communicable diseases in order to prevent or control them; providing emergency care for students in case of illness or injury; periodic practice in emergency evacuation procedures; provisions for physical fitness programs suited to the age, maturity, and physical capacity of each student; utilizing health services provided by community agencies.

Staff members, custodial help, and all school personnel cooperate in instituting methods and programs that protect and insure student health and safety. Students are supervised correctly in all school activities by adult personnel in accordance with state or local regulations.

In planning and organizing school health and safety services, the school recognizes the combined responsibilities of parents, public health agencies, social workers, civil defense officials, physicians, and dentists. The entire program is closely related to group and individual guidance and counseling services.

School health and safety services have great potential value in fostering the growth of future American citizens. Students are led to realize that health of mind is closely related to health of body and that each is essential to the development of their God-given powers. Furthermore, handicapped students and their parents are advised to accept the handicap and to cooperate with God's plan for them. Lastly, students should develop an appreciation of their physical well-being, an awareness of their moral and social responsibilities, and a concerned zeal for the physical well-being of their neighbor.

NAME OF SCHOOL_____ DATE_____

ADDRESS_____

(ARCH)DIOCESE OF_____

SELF-EVALUATION MEMBERS_____

_____

_____

Instructions

When undertaking a self-evaluation the members of the school staff should use the statement of GUIDING PRINCIPLES and CHECKLIST items as an aid to determining the extent to which their school program coincides with the Philosophy and Objectives of the school and meets the needs of the school population and community served. Of necessity a staff will modify statements of Guiding Principles, Checklist items and Evaluations to conform with the philosophy and characteristics of the particular school doing the evaluation. Wherever changes are made the school should explain under Comments the reasons for the change in relation to its own program. Minor differences in terminology should not be regarded as significant items of change.

CHECKLISTS

Checklist items consist of statements deemed applicable to the area of the Criteria being evaluated. These are suggested ideas and are not to be interpreted as the only statements applicable to the area or as all-inclusive. A school may wish to add additional statements of its own that will explain further the particular program of the school. Space is provided in each Checklist for such additions. If the change is regarded as significant, the school will use the letter C in the Checklist as indicated in the following instructions and explain under Comments the precise nature of its offerings.

A staff should note that a definite relation pertains between Checklist items and Evaluations. Members of the staff should familiarize themselves with the definite meanings of Checklist symbols and Evaluation ratings.

CHECKLIST items may be indicated as follows:

E—The statement or condition is *extensive* in application.

M—The statement or condition is *moderately* achieved.

L—The statement or condition is limited in application.

MN—The condition is missing but judged needed by the staff.

N—The condition does not apply to this school.

*C—The condition is achieved in a manner different from Checklist items.

    * Wherever C is used, this aim should be stated in one of the additional numbers of the Checklist and explained under COMMENTS.

EVALUATIONS

Evaluations represent numerical summations of the Checklist items. The rating is determined from discussions of the staff as related to the consistency of the school program with stated Philosophy and Objectives.

To secure a composite view of the school's outcomes in each area of the Criteria, a school will project the Evaluation ratings to the X Blank of the respective areas. A further picture of the total program will be secured by tabulating the Average of the X Blank on the Graphic Summary provided in the Y Blank. Instructions for such procedure are listed in the X and Y Blanks.

Evaluations are indicated as follows:

5—The condition is excellent and extensive. (Please note that 5 does not mean "perfect.")

4—The condition is very good. A school may care to use a further refinement of 4a or 4b: 4a indicates that the condition is extensive and functioning well; 4b indicates that the condition is moderately extensive but functioning excellently.

3—The condition meets student needs to a reasonable degree.

2—The condition is in need of *achievable* improvement.

1—The condition is not being achieved and its need is not recognized.

*MN—The condition is missing but needed.

 *N—The condition does not apply.

    * When MN or N are accepted by the staff for an *Evaluation* rating the divisor on the X Blank must be adjusted accordingly. N should not be used in CHECKLISTS and EVALUATIONS unless the condition absolutely DOES NOT APPLY. If the item is educationally desirable the school should not use N simply because it does not make use of the item. An adequate replacement for the item may fulfill the conditions of the Checklist.

I. General Nature and Organization

Organization for school health and safety services will vary according to state legislation, the wide diversity of school population, available facilities, administrative regulations, and allocated personnel.

CHECKLIST

(   ) 1. Health and safety services are provided as part of the elementary school program.

(   ) 2. Health and safety services are co-ordinated with those of the community.

(   ) 3. An effective and inclusive organizational pattern outlines the specific functions and responsibilities of administrators, teachers, and other personnel.

(   ) 4. Teacher duties and responsibilities in the program are periodically reviewed.

(   ) 5. Policies and procedures of the health and safety program are clearly defined in written form.

(   ) 6. A periodic evaluation of the health and safety program is made.

(   ) 7. The school initiates meetings with parents, health and safety agencies, and other interested community groups to discuss aims and purposes of the program.

(   ) 8. Periodic appraisal of the health status of students is required.

(   ) 9. Periodic appraisal of the health status of school personnel is required.

(   ) 10. Information regarding their health status is given to students, their parents, and other persons concerned.

(   ) 11. Health services offer assistance in discovering and educating exceptional children.

(   ) 12. Through individual counseling, parents are encouraged to take advantage of available treatment for adjustment of remediable defects of their children.

(   ) 13. The administration cooperates with recommendations offered by the school medical advisor and public health agencies.

(   ) 14. A guide for emergency care of illnesses and accidents is available from health officials.

(   ) 15. Training of teachers in first aid procedures is provided through community agencies.

(   ) 16. Cooperation with civil defense regulations exists.

(   ) 17. Adequate orientation in safety and health measures in case of disaster by fire, flood, tornado, hurricane, earthquake, and radioactive fallout is provided for students and school personnel.

(   ) 18. Student safety is controlled by regularly scheduled fire drills.

(   ) 19. Adequate provision is made to insure the safety of students in transit.

(   ) 20. A sound program in physical fitness is incorporated in the physical education program.

(   ) 21. Student recreation periods are co-ordinated and supervised by adult personnel.

(   ) 22. Health and safety program in the elementary school articulates with that of the secondary school.

(   ) 23.

(   ) 24.

SUPPLEMENTARY DATA

Supply a form indicating the organization of the school health and safety services with diagrams and appropriate descriptions and designate administrative responsibilities and interrelationships with the instructional staff and community groups.

EVALUATIONS

(   ) *a. How extensive are the provisions for school health services?*

(   ) *b. How extensive are the provisions for school safety services?*

(   ) *c. To what extent are the purposes of the health services program understood by the staff?*

(   ) *d. To what extent are the purposes of the safety services program understood by the staff?*

(   ) *e. To what extent are the school health services coordinated with community health objectives?*

(   ) *f. To what extent are the school safety services coordinated with community safety objectives?*

(   ) *g. To what extent does the school receive assistance from municipal and community health and safety services?*

COMMENTS

II. School Health and Safety Services

A. HEALTH APPRAISAL RECORDS

Health needs or handicaps of students are identified, recorded, and interpreted to parents.

CHECKLIST

(   ) 1. Cumulative health records for each student are on file.

(   ) 2. Periodic screening tests for hearing impairment are provided.

(   ) 3. There are periodic screening tests for vision impairment.

(   ) 4. Dental examinations are encouraged and/or provided.

(   ) 5. State or local requirements regarding medical examinations are observed.

(   ) 6. The administration cooperates with visiting health personnel, informing parents of student health problems and recommending follow-up.

(   ) 7. Parents are guided in securing proper help or treatment for the handicapped.

(   ) 8. Classroom teachers make necessary modifications to meet the needs of handicapped children enrolled in regular classes.

(   ) 9. Through counseling, parents and students are encouraged to accept handicaps in cooperation with God's plan.

(   ) 10. Health records of elementary school graduates are sent to secondary school attended by student.

(   ) 11.

(   ) 12.

EVALUATIONS

(   ) a. *How adequately do health appraisal procedures ensure the physical well-being of each student?*

(   ) b. *How adequately does the home-school cooperation ensure the physical well-being of each student?*

(   ) c. *To what extent does the school cooperate with other elementary schools and secondary schools in transfer of health records?*

COMMENTS

B. CONTROL OF COMMUNICABLE DISEASES

The responsibility for control of communicable diseases rests with the state or local health authorities. Effective community control programs require the full cooperation of school personnel.

CHECKLIST

( ) 1. School authorities encourage parental vigilance in the prevention and spread of communicable diseases.

( ) 2. The school staff observes students for signs and symptoms of communicable disease.

( ) 3. Students and staff are required to remain at home when ill with a communicable disease.

( ) 4. Upon discovery of any serious communicable disease, adequate safety precautions are taken for the remainder of the student and personnel body.

( ) 5. Students are acquainted with their moral responsibility to assist in the prevention of communicable disease by observing prescribed health regulations.

( ) 6. Disease control measures, such as vaccination and inoculation, are promoted.

( ) 7.

( ) 8.

EVALUATIONS

( ) *a. To what extent are the school policies and procedure effective for prevention and control of communicable diseases?*

( ) *b. To what extent is home-school cooperation effective for prevention and control of communicable diseases?*

COMMENTS

C. PROVISIONS FOR EMERGENCIES

Emergency procedures are an essential part of school health and safety services.

CHECKLIST

(   ) 1. First-aid supplies are conveniently located.

(   ) 2. Each teacher has available in written form, established policies for care of illness or injury.

(   ) 3. Reports of all serious accidents are kept on file.

(   ) 4. Students may avail themselves of accident insurance.

(   ) 5. Staff and students are familiar with procedures to be followed in case of fire or other public disaster.

(   ) 6. Parents or guardians are notified by school authorities immediately of student injury or illness.

(   ) 7. Injured or ill students are released only with the permission of parents or authorized individuals.

(   ) 8. Immediate medical attention is provided for serious injuries.

(   ) 9. Information concerning persons to be notified in emergencies is available.

(   ) 10. A person qualified in first-aid is available during school hours.

(   ) 11. Students are alerted to minimal first-aid procedures in health classes.

(   ) 12. Students are directed to exercise consideration toward others in times of emergency.

(   ) 13.

(   ) 14.

EVALUATIONS

(   ) *a. How adequately does the school health program meet emergencies involving illness or injury?*

(   ) *b. How adequately does the school safety program meet emergencies involving illness or injury?*

COMMENTS

D. PROMOTING HEALTHFUL AND SAFE SCHOOL LIVING

Administrators, teachers, custodians, community health and safety personnel cooperate to insure the successful realization of the school's health and safety programs.

CHECKLIST

( ) 1. Periodic inspection of the school plant is conducted by local health and safety agencies.

( ) 2. A consciousness of proper lighting and ventilation in each classroom is evident.

( ) 3. Mental and emotional reactions of students to the school organization are considered in the formulation of policies.

( ) 4. Teachers are assisted in understanding the needs of students and their problems by health personnel such as doctors, psychiatrists, etc.

( ) 5. School personnel cooperate with private and community agencies to promote sound mental and physical health of students.

( ) 6. School plant equipment and facilities are controlled and regulated by adequate safety devices.

( ) 7. Adequate facilities for fire control (sprinkler system, fire doors, number of exits in classrooms, etc.) are incorporated in the school plant.

( ) 8. Directions for exiting in case of fire are posted in each classroom.

( ) 9. Students are supervised in all school activities in accordance with state and local regulations.

( ) 10. Periodic checks of the physical education equipment are conducted.

( ) 11. Custodial services provide for daily cleaning of classrooms and other general facilities.

( ) 12. All units of the school building evidence an appropriate neatness, orderliness, and attractiveness.

( ) 13. Lavatories are adequately equipped with facilities for handwashing, including soap and towels.

( ) 14. Provision is made for a pleasant operation of the lunch program.

( ) 15. Adequate time is allotted for lunch.

( ) 16. The varying health needs of students are considered in all planning and scheduling of the school program.

( ) 17.

( ) 18.

EVALUATIONS

( ) a. *How successful are the school measures to ensure healthful and safe school living?*

( ) b. *How extensively are the services of the local health agencies used in the school?*

( ) c. *How extensively are the services of the local safety agencies used in the school?*

( ) d. *How adequate are the custodial services?*

COMMENTS

III. Special Characteristics of School Health and Safety Services

1. In which areas of the school's health and safety services are the objectives of the program being carried out most satisfactorily?

    a.

    b.

    c.

2. Which areas of the school's health and safety services need improvement?

    a.

    b.

    c.

3. In what ways have the school's health and safety services received recent consideration?

    a.

    b.

    c.

4. What aspects of the program are being improved at the present time or will be improved in the immediate future?

    a.

    b.

    c.

IV. General Evaluation of School Health and Safety Services

EVALUATIONS

(   ) *a. How adequately do the school's health and safety services relate to the objectives, philosophy, and purposes given in Section B?*

(   ) *b. How adequately do the school's health and safety services care for the individual requirements of the students?*

(   ) *c. How adequately are the needs of the school's health and safety services being recognized and met?*

COMMENTS

Formulated and Edited by the Criteria Committee, Elementary School
Department of The National Catholic Educational Association

School Plant

GUIDING PRINCIPLES

The school plant, which includes the site, buildings, equipment, and play areas, is the basic physical element in the function of the educational program. It provides the environment in which the staff and students work to achieve desirable learning outcomes.

The best possible use is made of the natural physical features of the site. Grounds about the buildings are well-kept and as attractive as possible.

A variety of classrooms, all-purpose areas and specially designated rooms meet the educational needs of students and staff. Design of buildings is flexible enough to permit conversion and future expansion.

Equipment and services provide for adequate illumination, water, heat, ventilation, and sanitation to comply with health, fire and safety code requirements. Outdoor and indoor recreational areas are equipped with sufficient and safe facilities.

The entire school plant provides the best possible learning atmosphere. A well-designed attractive and functional plant stimulates the community, as well as the student body, to use its facilities effectively.

NAME OF SCHOOL_____ DATE_____

ADDRESS_____

(ARCH)DIOCESE OF_____

SELF-EVALUATION MEMBERS_____

_____

_____

Instructions

When undertaking a self-evaluation the members of the school staff should use the statement of GUIDING PRINCIPLES and CHECKLIST items as an aid to determining the extent to which their school program coincides with the Philosophy and Objectives of the school and meets the needs of the school population and community served. Of necessity a staff will modify statements of Guiding Principles, Checklist items and Evaluations to conform with the philosophy and characteristics of the particular school doing the evaluation. Wherever changes are made the school should explain under Comments the reasons for the change in relation to its own program. Minor differences in terminology should not be regarded as significant items of change.

CHECKLISTS

Checklist items consist of statements deemed applicable to the area of the Criteria being evaluated. These are suggested ideas and are not to be interpreted as the only statements applicable to the area or as all-inclusive. A school may wish to add additional statements of its own that will explain further the particular program of the school. Space is provided in each Checklist for such additions. If the change is regarded as significant, the school will use the letter C in the Checklist as indicated in the following instructions and explain under Comments the precise nature of its offerings.

A staff should note that a definite relation pertains between Checklist items and Evaluations. Members of the staff should familiarize themselves with the definite meanings of Checklist symbols and Evaluation ratings.

CHECKLIST items may be indicated as follows:

E—The statement or condition is *extensive* in application.

M—The statement or condition is *moderately* achieved.

L—The statement or condition is limited in application.

MN—The condition is missing but judged needed by the staff.

N—The condition does not apply to this school.

*C—The condition is achieved in a manner different from Checklist items.

   * Wherever C is used, this aim should be stated in one of the additional numbers of the Checklist and explained under COMMENTS.

EVALUATIONS

Evaluations represent numerical summations of the Checklist items. The rating is determined from discussions of the staff as related to the consistency of the school program with stated Philosophy and Objectives.

To secure a composite view of the school's outcomes in each area of the Criteria, a school will project the Evaluation ratings to the X Blank of the respective areas. A further picture of the total program will be secured by tabulating the Average of the X Blank on the Graphic Summary provided in the Y Blank. Instructions for such procedure are listed in the X and Y Blanks.

Evaluations are indicated as follows:

5—The condition is excellent and extensive. (Please note that 5 does not mean "perfect.")

4—The condition is very good. A school may care to use a further refinement of 4a or 4b: 4a indicates that the condition is extensive and functioning well; 4b indicates that the condition is moderately extensive but functioning excellently.

3—The condition meets student needs to a reasonable degree.

2—The condition is in need of *achievable* improvement.

1—The condition is not being achieved and its need is not recognized.

*MN—The condition is missing but needed.

 *N—The condition does not apply.

   * When MN or N are accepted by the staff for an *Evaluation* rating the divisor on the X Blank must be adjusted accordingly. N should not be used in CHECKLISTS and EVALUATIONS unless the condition absolutely DOES NOT APPLY. If the item is educationally desirable the school should not use N simply because it does not make use of the item. An adequate replacement for the item may fulfill the conditions of the Checklist.

I. Site

A. LOCATION

CHECKLIST

The location of the site:

( ) 1. is as near as possible to the center of present and expected future school population.
( ) 2. can be easily reached by the school population.
( ) 3. is accessible via paved roads, streets or walks.
( ) 4. is reasonably free from traffic and transportation hazards.
( ) 5. is reasonably free from neighborhood noises.
( ) 6. is free from air pollution by fumes, dust, smoke, etc.

( ) 7. provides adequate light and air.
( ) 8. permits proper drainage of surface water.
( ) 9. has adequate sewer disposal facilities.
( ) 10. has an adequate water supply available.
( ) 11. has easily accessible fire hydrants.

( ) 12.

( ) 13.

EVALUATIONS

( ) *a. How accessible is the site to the school population served?*
( ) *b. How adequately does the site provide a favorable learning environment?*
( ) *c. How adequately does the site provide for health and safety?*

COMMENTS

B. PHYSICAL CHARACTERISTICS

CHECKLIST

The site:

( ) 1. has sufficient acreage to provide for the needs of the school.

( ) 2. has grounds spacious enough for anticipated expansion needs.

( ) 3. has adequate play areas.

( ) 4. has play areas located so as not to disturb classes.

( ) 5. has hard-surfaced driveways and walks.

( ) 6. has passageways and grounds free from hazards to students on their way to and from play areas.

( ) 7. has adequate parking areas.

( ) 8. has provisions for safe loading and unloading of students transported to school by car or bus.

( ) 9. is enhanced by attractive landscaping.

( ) 10. has specified routes and parking facilities for bicycles.

( ) 11.

( ) 12.

EVALUATIONS

( ) *a. To what extent is the site adequate for student enrollment?*

( ) *b. To what extent is the site adequate for student activities?*

( ) *c. To what extent do school grounds conform to good aesthetic taste?*

( ) *d. To what extent are school grounds safeguarded against accidents to students, faculty and community?*

COMMENTS

II. The Building or Buildings

CHECKLIST

( ) 1. The building is so situated that efficient use is made of the entire area.

( ) 2. The exterior of the building is attractive.

( ) 3. Provision is made for future expansion.

( ) 4. Construction eliminates concealed spaces where gases can accumulate and become hazards.

( ) 5. The building is durable and fire-resistant.

( ) 6. Roof is durable with adequate drainage.

( ) 7. Sufficient number of rooms is provided to meet student needs.

( ) 8. Some rooms have non-supporting partitions.

( ) 9. Non-usable space is at a minimum.

( ) 10. Provision is made for truck deliveries without interference in school activities.

( ) 11. Doors open outward.

( ) 12. Exit doors are equipped with panic bars, etc.

( ) 13. Exits are clearly marked.

( ) 14. Construction and electrical installations meet building code requirements.

( ) 15. Stairways and corridors are free from storage.

( ) 16. Stairwells are enclosed.

( ) 17. Stairways have adequate, continuous hand-rails.

( ) 18. Stairs are provided with safety treads.

( ) 19. Floor coverings are fire-resistant.

( ) 20. Acoustic control is adequate.

( ) 21. Lockers and/or coatrooms are adequate.

( ) 22. Heating plant provides sufficient heat to all areas.

( ) 23. Heating plant has an outside entrance.

( ) 24. Interiors of buildings are attractive.

( ) 25. Provision is made for student safety and health when enroute between buildings.

( ) 26. When building is used outside school hours attention is given to: (Check items)
_____ adequate parking space.
_____ lighting of parking areas.
_____ heating of used areas.
_____ lighted entrances and exits.
_____ protection of unused facilities.
_____ accessible and lighted lavatories.
_____ auditorium facilities.
_____ gymnasium availability.

( ) 27. Building is equipped with air-conditioning or automatic ventilating system.

( ) 28. Elevator service is provided.

( ) 29. Bulletin boards and display cases are provided.

( ) 30. Provision is made for safe and effective use of multi-sensory materials.

( ) 31. Provision is made for educational TV.

( ) 32. Provision is made for closed circuit TV.

( ) 33. Emergency electrical power is installed.

( ) 34. Safety glass is used in windows and doors.

( ) 35. Provision is made for adequate storage of school supplies.

( ) 36.

( ) 37.

EVALUATIONS

( ) *a. To what extent do stairways meet the need of the students?*

( ) *b. To what extent do corridors meet the need of students?*

( ) *c. To what extent do exits meet need of students?*

( ) *d. How effectively does the building provide for health of students?*

( ) *e. How effectively does the building provide for safety of students?*

( ) *f. How adequately does the school building meet needs of the community?*

COMMENTS

III. Building Services

A. ILLUMINATION

CHECKLIST

( ) 1. Lighting conditions make it possible for visual tasks to be done efficiently and without strain.

( ) 2. The surface area and fenestration provide a satisfactory amount of daylight.

( ) 3. Comfort and efficiency in vision are provided by non-gloss surfaces.

( ) 4. Natural lighting is controlled.

( ) 5. Standard light intensities are maintained.

( ) 6. Wall and floor colors are chosen to secure desirable brightness and balance.

( ) 7. Adequate lighting is provided for corridors.

( ) 8. Adequate lighting is provided for lavatories.

( ) 9. Adequate lighting is provided for stairways.

( ) 10. Illumination of all rooms and areas is adjustable to varying needs.

( ) 11.

( ) 12.

EVALUATIONS

( ) *a. How adequate is the quantity of illumination?*

( ) *b. How adequate is the quality of illumination?*

( ) *c. To what extent is proper use made of illumination facilities?*

COMMENTS

B. TEMPERATURE AND VENTILATION

CHECKLIST

( ) 1. Temperature and ventilation are regulated in each classroom by an easily accessible thermostat.

( ) 2. A temperature of 68° to 72°F is maintained.

( ) 3. Controlled air circulation is provided in all areas.

( ) 4. Provision is made for air purification.

( ) 5. Specific provision is made for proper ventilation of lockers, locker rooms, gymnasium, and science room.

( ) 6. Specific provision is made for proper ventilation of lavatories.

( ) 7. Specific provision is made for proper ventilation of corridors and stairways.

( ) 8.

( ) 9.

EVALUATIONS

( ) *a. To what extent is proper temperature maintained?*

( ) *b. To what extent is proper ventilation maintained?*

( ) *c. To what extent does the heating and ventilating system provide for varied needs?*

COMMENTS

C. WATER AND SANITATION

CHECKLIST

(   ) 1. Drinking fountains are sufficient to meet student need.

(   ) 2. Drinking fountains are of proper height.

(   ) 3. Hygienic conditions for drinking water are maintained.

(   ) 4. Adequate toilet and lavatories are provided for boys, girls, faculty members.

(   ) 5. Lavatory walls and floors are easy to maintain.

(   ) 6. Hot and cold water are provided.

(   ) 7. Plumbing is kept in good repair.

(   ) 8. Entrances and exits ensure privacy.

(   ) 9. Mirrors are provided in lavatories.

(   ) 10. Adequate supplies of soap, towels or driers, and toilet tissue are provided.

(   ) 11. Desirable standards of sanitation are maintained in all lavatories.

(   ) 12.

(   ) 13.

EVALUATIONS

(   ) a. *How adequate are drinking fountains to meet need of students?*

(   ) b. *How satisfactory is the location of lavatories?*

(   ) c. *How adequate are lavatory facilities?*

(   ) d. *How adequate are lavatory supplies?*

(   ) e. *How satisfactory is the maintenance of lavatories?*

COMMENTS

D. MISCELLANEOUS SERVICES

CHECKLIST

(   )   1. Custodial closets are adequate for needs.

(   )   2. Custodial closets are conveniently located.

(   )   3. Custodial equipment is adequate.

(   )   4. Hot and cold water is provided in custodial closets.

(   )   5. Provision is made for proper disposal of wastes.

(   )   6. Repair and maintenance are provided.

(   )   7. Provision is made for adequate storage space.

(   )   8. Electrical wiring conforms to code regulations.

(   )   9. Fire extinguishers are accessible and checked at definite times.

(   ) 10. Fire inspections are made regularly.

(   ) 11. Fire signals differ from other signals.

(   ) 12. Fire alarm system is in working order at all times.

(   ) 13. Fire alarms conform to code regulations.

(   ) 14. Combustible materials are properly stored and safeguarded.

(   ) 15. Emergency lighting conforms to code regulations.

(   ) 16. Areas under stairwells are kept free of storage.

(   ) 17. Boiler room is free of combustible material.

(   ) 18.

(   ) 19.

EVALUATIONS

(   )   *a. How adequate are custodial facilities?*

(   )   *b. How adequate is custodial equipment?*

(   )   *c. To what extent is equipment for fire protection adequate?*

(   )   *d. To what extent are miscellaneous services periodically checked for maximum efficiency?*

COMMENTS

IV. Classrooms

CHECKLIST

( ) 1. Sufficient space is provided for effective teaching of class enrollment.

( ) 2. Classroom arrangement provides for flexibility in varying situations.

( ) 3. Windows are provided with suitable equipment for control of light.

( ) 4. Darkening facilities are provided for effective use of visual aids.

( ) 5. Provision is made for effective acoustics.

( ) 6. Floors are of a material that is easily maintained.

( ) 7. Desks are arranged to make effective use of light.

( ) 8. Desks are maintained in good condition.

( ) 9. Furnishings conform to standards for height, comfort and good posture.

( ) 10. Classrooms have direct communication with main office.

( ) 11. Adequate chalkboards are provided in each classroom.

( ) 12. Adequate corkboards are provided in each classroom.

( ) 13. Adequate map rails, peg board, and other display materials are provided in each classroom.

( ) 14. A crucifix is in evidence in each classroom.

( ) 15. The American flag is properly displayed in each classroom.

( ) 16. Classroom interiors are attractive and in good taste.

( ) 17. Sufficient storage room is provided.

( ) 18. Electrical outlets are sufficient in number and power and easily accessible.

( ) 19. Facilities for storing teachers' personal effects are provided.

( ) 20. A thermometer is provided for each classroom.

( ) 21.

( ) 22.

EVALUATIONS

( ) a. How adequate are classrooms for size of class accommodated?

( ) b. How adequate is standard classroom equipment?

( ) c. How satisfactory is general provision for health of students in classroom?

( ) d. How effectively do classrooms suggest desirable aesthetic standards to students?

COMMENTS

V. Special Rooms and Services

A. AUDITORIUM

CHECKLIST

(   )   1. The auditorium is conveniently located.
(   )   2. Exits meet code requirements.
(   )   3. Size of auditorium meets the needs of school and community
(   )   4. Seating is adequate.
(   )   5. Design and furnishings are in good taste.
(   )   6. Acoustics are satisfactory.
(   )   7. Ventilation is adequate.
(   )   8. Public address system is satisfactory.
(   )   9. Lighting is adequate.
(   ) 10. An adequate stage is provided.
(   ) 11. Stage curtains, hangings and improvised scenery meet code requirements.

(   ) 12. Provisions are made for darkening the auditorium.
(   ) 13. Sufficient space is provided for storage of stage properties.
(   ) 14. Stage lights are equipped with suitable controls.
(   ) 15. Adequate stage entrances and exits are provided.
(   ) 16. Safety precautions are observed.
(   ) 17. Lavatories are located near auditorium.
(   ) 18. Check rooms are available.
(   ) 19.
(   ) 20.

EVALUATIONS

(   ) *a. How adequate are size and seating facilities of the auditorium?*
(   ) *b. How adequate are the stage and its facilities?*
(   ) *c. How adequately does the auditorium meet existing fire and safety code regulations?*
(   ) *d. To what extent does the auditorium reflect good taste in its decoration?*

COMMENTS

B. GYMNASIUM

CHECKLIST

(   ) 1. The gymnasium is conveniently located.
(   ) 2. Adequate entrances and exits are provided.
(   ) 3. Size meets the needs of students and community.
(   ) 4. Heating is satisfactory.
(   ) 5. Ventilation is satisfactory.
(   ) 6. Equipment is adequate.
(   ) 7. Equipment is in good condition.

(   ) 8. Storage facilities are provided.
(   ) 9. Dressing rooms are in proximity to gymnasium.
(   ) 10. Shower facilities are provided.
(   ) 11. Adequate seating is provided.
(   ) 12. Safety precautions are observed.
(   ) 13.
(   ) 14.

EVALUATIONS

(   ) a. *How adequate is the size of the gymnasium?*
(   ) b. *How adequate is equipment used in the gymnasium?*
(   ) c. *To what extent is the gymnasium used for a physical education program?*
(   ) d. *To what extent does the gymnasium provide for community needs?*
(   ) e. *How adequate are provisions for safety in the gymnasium?*

COMMENTS

C. CAFETERIA FACILITIES

CHECKLIST

(   ) 1. The lunchroom is large enough to accommodate the student body.
(   ) 2. Heating is satisfactory.
(   ) 3. Ventilation is satisfactory.
(   ) 4. Natural and artificial lighting is adequate.
(   ) 5. Furniture and fixtures are simple in design, durable and attractive.
(   ) 6. Equipment in lunchroom is adequate.
(   ) 7. Floor surface is easily maintained.
(   ) 8. Lunchroom is provided for faculty.
(   ) 9. Acoustic control is adequate.
(   ) 10. Sanitary drinking water facilities are provided.

(   ) 11. Provision is made for disposal of waste paper, etc.
(   ) 12. Lavatories are conveniently located.
(   ) 13. Kitchen has efficient and sanitary cooking equipment.
(   ) 14. Dishwashing facilities are adequate.
(   ) 15. Kitchen has outside delivery door.
(   ) 16. Storage facilities are adequate.
(   ) 17. Refrigeration facilities are adequate.
(   ) 18. Walls and floors of kitchen can be easily maintained.
(   ) 19.
(   ) 20.

EVALUATIONS

(   ) *a. How adequate is capacity of lunchroom?*
(   ) *b. How adequate is equipment in lunchroom?*
(   ) *c. To what extent does lunchroom meet aesthetic standards?*
(   ) *d. How adequate is size of kitchen?*
(   ) *e. How adequate is kitchen equipment?*
(   ) *f. How satisfactory are maintenance conditions?*

SUPPLEMENTARY DATA

1. Seating capacity of lunchroom...————
2. Seating capacity of dining room...————
3. Number of shifts necessary...————

COMMENTS

D. INSTRUCTIONAL MATERIALS CENTER

CHECKLIST

(   ) 1. The instructional materials center is easily accessible.

(   ) 2. Adequate space is provided for housing and convenient arrangement of instructional materials and equipment.

(   ) 3. The reading room provides space according to accepted standards.

(   ) 4. Furnishings and fixed equipment are in accord with accepted library standards.

(   ) 5. Provision is made for storage.

(   ) 6. Work area is provided for librarian.

(   ) 7. Lighting facilities are adequate.

(   ) 8. Acoustics are satisfactory.

(   ) 9. Library is attractive and in good taste.

(   ) 10. Provision is made for a remedial and developmental work center.

(   ) 11.

(   ) 12.

EVALUATIONS

(   ) a. *How adequate is size of instructional materials center to serve the needs of the school population?*

(   ) b. *To what extent do materials center furnishings meet accepted standards?*

(   ) c. *How adequate are provisions for housing instructional materials and equipment?*

COMMENTS

E. OFFICE AND STAFF ROOMS

CHECKLIST

(   ) 1. The administration center is conveniently located.

(   ) 2. The principal has a private office.

(   ) 3. School secretary or clerk has an office properly equipped.

(   ) 4. Administration office provides for mail and bulletin facilities.

(   ) 5. Storage space for office supplies is provided.

(   ) 6. Permanent records are kept in a locked fire-resistant file.

(   ) 7. Reception area is located near administration office.

(   ) 8. Inter-communication system is provided.

(   ) 9. Automatic bell system is provided.

(   ) 10. Faculty rooms are adequate in accommodations: (Check)
_____ lounge
_____ lunch room
_____ lavatory
_____ meeting room

(   ) 11. Sufficient phones are installed.

(   ) 12.

(   ) 13.

EVALUATIONS

(   ) a. *How convenient is the location of administration center?*

(   ) b. *How adequate is the space provided for administration center?*

(   ) c. *How adequate is equipment in school offices?*

(   ) d. *How adequate are provisions for faculty rooms?*

COMMENTS

F. CLINIC OR HEALTH ROOM

CHECKLIST

( ) 1. Space is provided for health services.
( ) 2. Necessary health service equipment is easily accessible.
( ) 3. First-aid equipment is available.
( ) 4. Health clinic is provided with bed or cot.

( ) 5. Files are available for health records.
( ) 6. Lavatory facilities are accessible.
( ) 7.
( ) 8.

EVALUATIONS

( ) a. How adequate are facilities for health services?
( ) b. How adequate are facilities for first-aid?

COMMENTS

The following items apply if the school conducts the transportation service or if the service is sublet under contract to a private firm.

VI. School Buses

CHECKLIST

( ) 1. Bus transportation is provided for students.
( ) 2. Legal standards for transportation of students by bus are observed.
( ) 3. Buses are maintained in a safe operating condition.
( ) 4. Buses are equipped with materials necessary for minor repairs.
( ) 5. Buses are equipped with a first-aid kit.

( ) 6. Buses are equipped with fire and safety equipment.
( ) 7. A specified and safe area is designated for boarding, unloading, and parking buses.
( ) 8.
( ) 9.

EVALUATIONS

( ) a. How adequate are facilities for bus transportation of students?
( ) b. To what extent do buses and equipment conform to required legal standards?
( ) c. How adequate are facilities for maintenance of bus in accordance with safety regulations?

COMMENTS

VII. Special Characteristics of School Plant

1. What are the outstanding characteristics of this school plant?

   a.

   b.

   c.

2. What is the greatest need for improvement?

   a.

   b.

   c.

   d.

3. What improvements have been made in the past three years?

   a.

   b.

   c.

4. What improvements in the school plant are now being made or are definitely planned for the immediate future?

   a.

   b.

   c.

5. What carefully conducted studies has the school made or is making of its own problems related to the school plant?

   a.

   b.

   c.

VIII. General Evaluations of the School Plant

EVALUATIONS

(   ) *a. To what extent is the school plant consistent with the school's philosophy?*
(   ) *b. To what extent does the school plant meet the needs of students and community?*
(   ) *c. To what extent is the school identifying problems in the school plant and seeking their solution?*

Formulated and Edited by the Criteria Committee, Elementary School
Department of The National Catholic Educational Association

Administration and School Staff

GUIDING PRINCIPLES

The responsibility of providing a sound, modern and Catholic educational program for all students in the elementary schools depends mainly on the administration and staff. The immediate administration of the school system rests upon the superintendent of schools, under the direction of the Ordinary of the diocese. The diocesan school board acts as an advisory group and recommends to the Ordinary matters pertaining to the welfare of the Catholic schools of the diocese. Supervisors, either diocesan or community, are responsible to the superintendent of schools for implementing diocesan school policies. They serve in the capacity of consultants to the superintendent and to the administrators and staff of the schools they supervise. The pastor of the parish delegates to the principal the authority to organize and administer the program of the school.

The functions of administration, organization, and teaching must conform to the principles of Catholic philosophy of education. Therefore, the primary commitment of the administration and staff is to crystallize and implement the objectives of Catholic education.

The duties of administration include leadership in the educational program, in supervision and improvement of instruction, in fostering community relations, and in management and maintenance of plant and facilities.

A competent staff is devoted to an appropriate educational program that includes the intellectual and spiritual development, as well as the physical and social well-being of the students. The staff strives to fulfill the philosophy, objectives, and functions of a Catholic elementary school. Members of the staff are qualified by preparation and experience to contribute to the attainment of educational goals.

The number of staff members varies according to school enrollment and special needs of students. The teaching load is such that maximum efficiency results. Salary scales are set up to meet standards that satisfy requirements of social justice, of professional preparation, and experience.

The principal strives to establish rapport with and among the members of the staff. Both administrator and staff enhance the educational program of the school through good public relations. They give service to the family, Church, and state by prudent participation in community and civic affairs. Both administrator and staff work to establish sound relationships with each other, with officials of local public schools, and with other members of the community.

The principal is the responsible agent for the proper functioning of the school. Administrative leadership is evident in comprehensive planning, coordinating, and evaluating all areas of the curriculum.

A spirit of cooperation strengthens administrative effectiveness. Through a democratic spirit and good will, promoted by sharing responsibilities with staff members, the administrator builds a unity of effort which results in a greater fulfillment of educational goals.

NAME OF SCHOOL_____ DATE_____

ADDRESS_____

(ARCH)DIOCESE OF_____

SELF-EVALUATION MEMBERS_____

_____

_____

Instructions

When undertaking a self-evaluation the members of the school staff should use the statement of GUIDING PRINCIPLES and CHECKLIST items as an aid to determining the extent to which their school program coincides with the Philosophy and Objectives of the school and meets the needs of the school population and community served. Of necessity a staff will modify statements of Guiding Principles, Checklist items and Evaluations to conform with the philosophy and characteristics of the particular school doing the evaluation. Wherever changes are made the school should explain under Comments the reasons for the change in relation to its own program. Minor differences in terminology should not be regarded as significant items of change.

CHECKLISTS

Checklist items consist of statements deemed applicable to the area of the Criteria being evaluated. These are suggested ideas and are not to be interpreted as the only statements applicable to the area or as all-inclusive. A school may wish to add additional statements of its own that will explain further the particular program of the school. Space is provided in each Checklist for such additions. If the change is regarded as significant, the school will use the letter C in the Checklist as indicated in the following instructions and explain under Comments the precise nature of its offerings.

A staff should note that a definite relation pertains between Checklist items and Evaluations. Members of the staff should familiarize themselves with the definite meanings of Checklist symbols and Evaluation ratings.

CHECKLIST items may be indicated as follows:

E—The statement or condition is *extensive* in application.

M—The statement or condition is *moderately* achieved.

L—The statement or condition is limited in application.

MN—The condition is missing but judged needed by the staff.

N—The condition does not apply to this school.

*C—The condition is achieved in a manner different from Checklist items.

* Wherever C is used, this aim should be stated in one of the additional numbers of the Checklist and explained under COMMENTS.

EVALUATIONS

Evaluations represent numerical summations of the Checklist items. The rating is determined from discussions of the staff as related to the consistency of the school program with stated Philosophy and Objectives.

To secure a composite view of the school's outcomes in each area of the Criteria, a school will project the Evaluation ratings to the X Blank of the respective areas. A further picture of the total program will be secured by tabulating the Average of the X Blank on the Graphic Summary provided in the Y Blank. Instructions for such procedure are listed in the X and Y Blanks.

Evaluations are indicated as follows:

5—The condition is excellent and extensive. (Please note that 5 does not mean "perfect.")

4—The condition is very good. A school may care to use a further refinement of 4a or 4b: 4a indicates that the condition is extensive and functioning well; 4b indicates that the condition is moderately extensive but functioning excellently.

3—The condition meets student needs to a reasonable degree.

2—The condition is in need of *achievable* improvement.

1—The condition is not being achieved and its need is not recognized.

*MN—The condition is missing but needed.

*N—The condition does not apply.

* When MN or N are accepted by the staff for an *Evaluation* rating the divisor on the X Blank must be adjusted accordingly. N should not be used in CHECKLISTS and EVALUATIONS unless the condition absolutely DOES NOT APPLY. If the item is educationally desirable the school should not use N simply because it does not make use of the item. An adequate replacement for the item may fulfill the conditions of the Checklist.

I. School Staff

A. NUMERICAL ADEQUACY

Indicate the number of staff members who devote all or part of their time to the elementary school for the current year 19_____–19_____.

Total school enrollment_____

Instructional Staff	Number of Staff Members		Total Full Time Equivalent of All Members*
	Full-time	Part-time	
1. Administrator (include Supervising Principal)			
2. Classroom Teachers			
3. Instructional materials center personnel			
4. Specialists and consultants (include guidance personnel)			
5. Nurse(s)			
6. Others			
TOTAL			
NONINSTRUCTIONAL STAFF			
1. Secretaries and clerks			
2. Cafeteria manager and assistants			
3. Custodians and maintenance workers			
4. Others			
TOTAL			

* 30 hours a week equals one full-time person.

SUPPLEMENTARY DATA

1. List administrative positions.
2. List supervisory positions.
3. Specify the duties of the instructional materials personnel.
4. Describe any assistance regularly received from the diocesan office, religious community, public school district, and/or other units.
5. Specify the services of the specialists and consultants.

EVALUATIONS

(　　) *a. How numerically adequate are the administrators?*
(　　) *b. How numerically adequate are the classroom teachers?*
(　　) *c. How numerically adequate is the professional non-instructional staff? See 1, 2, 3 of Noninstructional Staff chart.*
(　　) *d. How numerically adequate is the clerical staff?*
(　　) *e. How numerically adequate is the cafeteria staff?*
(　　) *f. How numerically adequate is the maintenance staff?*

COMMENTS

B. ADMINISTRATIVE STAFF

1. Diocesan School Board (Educational Advisory Board to the Ordinary)

CHECKLIST

The diocesan school board:

(   ) 1. has been selected by the Ordinary of the diocese to serve in an advisory capacity.

(   ) 2. holds regular meetings at least twice a year.

(   ) 3. assists the Ordinary in developing policies, organizations, and procedures in accordance with diocesan regulations.

(   ) 4. recognizes the diocesan superintendent as the delegate of the Ordinary in administration of the diocesan school system.

(   ) 5. deliberates as a group on the recommendations of the superintendent of schools concerning school matters.

(   ) 6. approves the annual budget for the diocesan school office.

(   ) 7. accepts the line and staff relationship of the diocesan school system in regard to communication with personnel of the system.

(   ) 8. assists in developing policies to protect staff and students from exploitation by individuals and groups.

(   ) 9. accepts from the superintendent the minutes of school board meetings and the periodical codification of policies and regulations.

(   ) 10. approves the program of studies, adoption of textbooks, and standards set up to insure high quality of education.

(   ) 11. assists in developing sound policies with regard to salaries of teachers, social security, insurance, sick leave, and retirement plans.

(   ) 12. approves the contractual forms for religious communities and lay teachers.

(   ) 13. approves regulations for certification of school personnel.

(   ) 14. approves plans for proposed school buildings.

(   ) 15. offers constructive suggestions for the improvement of the school program.

(   ) 16.

(   ) 17.

SUPPLEMENTARY DATA (*Private schools which are not under the jurisdiction of the diocesan school board, specify on a separate sheet the matter of jurisdiction.*)

EVALUATIONS

(   ) *a. To what extent does the school board work in conjunction with the superintendent?*

(   ) *b. To what extent is the diocesan school board active in developing sound administrative policies?*

(   ) *c. To what extent are the published policies of the diocesan school board observed?*

COMMENTS

2. The Superintendent of Schools

The following functions are commonly regarded as the special responsibility of the executive head of the school system, but their performance may be delegated to others.

CHECKLIST

The superintendent of schools:

(   ) 1. derives his authority from the Ordinary of the diocese whom he represents in the administration of school affairs.

(   ) 2. acts as an officer of the diocesan school board.

(   ) 3. keeps the diocesan school board informed regarding school objectives, achievements, needs, and future plans.

(   ) 4. assists the board in making sound decisions in matters of school policy.

(   ) 5. administers the diocesan school office.

(   ) 6. unifies the diocesan school system through the adoption of sound policies.

(   ) 7. utilizes help of the supervisory staff in formulating school policies.

(   ) 8. interprets the educational policies of the diocese for the public and specifically for those engaged in the work of education.

(   ) 9. interprets state and federal laws to the schools.

(   ) 10. makes sure that state requirements related to state school laws are met by diocesan schools.

(   ) 11. submits required reports to the state educational authorities.

(   ) 12. prepares and issues the school calendar in accordance with state and diocesan regulations.

(   ) 13. provides for a uniform system of pupil accounting.

(   ) 14. provides a curriculum in keeping with the aims of Catholic education.

(   ) 15. approves the curriculum of the schools in accordance with the standards specified by the state and diocese.

(   ) 16. sponsors research in curriculum areas.

(   ) 17. sponsors teacher institutes and workshops in various areas of curriculum.

(   ) 18. makes periodic visits to the schools.

(   ) 19. provides supervision of schools through community and diocesan supervisors and school principals.

(   ) 20. provides the schools with the services of consultants.

(   ) 21. secures the cooperation of diocesan staff personnel in regard to stated educational directives.

(   ) 22. coordinates the educational endeavors of religious communities in the diocese.

(   ) 23. recommends to schools qualified and experienced lay teachers.

(   ) 24. maintains adequate teacher records.

(   ) 25. prepares statistical reports of enrollment and teacher status, etc.

(   ) 26. evaluates the progress of the schools by means of diocesan-wide testing programs.

(   ) 27. initiates study and selection of textbooks through qualified committees.

(   ) 28. provides a department for central purchasing of school equipment and supplies.

(   ) 29. provides for utilization of public and private funds as an aid to solving financial problems.

(   ) 30. makes himself available for consultation and speaking engagements.

(   ) 31.

(   ) 32.

EVALUATIONS

(   ) a. *How adequate is the educational organization of the diocesan school office?*

(   ) b. *To what extent does the superintendent cooperate with state and local authorities?*

(   ) c. *To what extent is the school interpreted to the community?*

(   ) d. *How adequate is supervision provided by the diocesan school office?*

COMMENTS

3. The Supervisor

The supervisor, community or diocesan, works cooperatively with the diocesan superintendent and in harmony with the diocesan school board in rendering service to all teachers in the diocese.

A. *Preparation and Qualifications*

CHECKLIST

The supervisor:

( ) 1. has a liberal education.
( ) 2. has a thorough knowledge of Catholic philosophy of education.
( ) 3. has adequate professional education.
( ) 4. has had successful teaching experience in elementary schools.

( ) 5. has had successful administration experience in elementary schools.
( ) 6. is capable of inspiring and guiding professionally the administrator and staff.

EVALUATIONS

( ) *a. How adequate is the professional preparation of the supervisor?*
( ) *b. How extensive is the educational experience of the supervisor?*
( ) *c. To what extent is the supervisor capable of establishing rapport with school personnel?*

COMMENTS

B. *Duties and Functions*

CHECKLIST

The supervisor:

( ) 1. maintains an attitude of respect and loyalty to the personnel charged with education in the diocese.

( ) 2. observes diocesan school policies as approved by the diocesan board.

( ) 3. strives for professional and educational standards.

( ) 4. works to improve the teaching-learning situation.

( ) 5. cooperates with the superintendent in school-related activities.

( ) 6. attends meetings scheduled by the superintendent.

( ) 7. notifies superintendent of a visitation.

( ) 8. presents a report of the school to the pastor.

( ) 9. gives an evaluation of schools visited to the superintendent.

( ) 10. interprets diocesan educational policies to school personnel.

( ) 11. assists in coordinating school policies and procedures.

( ) 12. serves on curriculum committees.

( ) 13. interprets curriculum guides to teachers.

( ) 14. examines, analyzes, and recommends textbooks for adoption.

( ) 15. serves as a resource person in obtaining instructional materials.

( ) 16. cooperates with consultants and other supervisors.

( ) 17. assists in the program of in-service education for teachers.

( ) 18. participates in teacher education.

( ) 19. plans test evaluation programs.

( ) 20. utilizes current research in education.

( ) 21. is aware of the educational needs of the diocese and community.

( ) 22. directs and guides the principal in her role as administrator and supervisor.

( ) 23. assists the principal in the evaluation of instruction.

( ) 24. is available for consultation and speaking engagements.

( ) 25. schedules conferences with principal and teachers.

( ) 26. conducts faculty meetings.

( ) 27. arranges inter-school and/or inter-class visitations.

( ) 28. helps to plan effective enrichment and remedial programs.

( ) 29. recommends teachers for demonstration lessons.

( ) 30. participates in workshops and conventions at local, state, and national levels.

( ) 31. affiliates with professional organizations and encourages administrators and staff to hold membership.

( ) 32. keeps an up-to-date library of current professional and instructional literature.

( ) 33.

( ) 34.

EVALUATIONS

( ) *a. To what extent does the supervisor cooperate with the diocesan personnel?*

( ) *b. How adequate is the program of supervision?*

( ) *c. How effectively does the supervisor perform her duties?*

COMMENTS

4. The Pastor

The pastor is the head of the school and delegates his authority to the principal in educational matters. His authority comes directly from the Ordinary since all Catholic schools are under the jurisdiction of the Ordinary. The pastor's duties toward the school are of a spiritual, administrative, and financial nature.

CHECKLIST

The Pastor:

(   ) 1. delegates authority to the principal as a trained professional educator.

(   ) 2. confers frequently with the principal concerning school matters.

(   ) 3. deals with the teaching staff through the principal.

(   ) 4. develops parish school policy in accordance with diocesan regulations.

(   ) 5. promotes adherence to school calendar.

(   ) 6. assumes responsibility for the religious education of students.

(   ) 7. acts on recommendations made by the Ordinary or his delegate for the immediate improvement of the school.

(   ) 8. cooperates in all diocesan activities promoted through the school.

(   ) 9. provides full-time supervising principal for a school having eight teachers or more.

(   ) 10. provides part-time supervising principal for a school having fewer than eight teachers.

(   ) 11. provides the principal with sufficient funds for diocesan texts and for instructional material center supplies.

(   ) 12. provides adequate clerical assistance to principal.

(   ) 13. provides maintenance service for school building.

(   ) 14. implements local and state legislation in regard to the school.

(   ) 15. plans ahead for expansion and improvement of buildings and increase of staff members.

(   ) 16. relieves teachers of extraneous activities such as fund-raising, training choir and altar boys.

(   ) 17. provides suitable working conditions for staff members.

(   ) 18. exercises pastoral prudence in dealing with referrals and problem cases.

(   ) 19. encourages cooperation with community agencies.

(   ) 20. encourages interest in the school on the part of parents and other members of the community.

(   ) 21. promotes an active home and school association devoted to educational discussion.

(   ) 22. makes a reasonable effort to have graduates placed in Catholic secondary schools and shows continued interest in their progress.

(   ) 23. arranges for consultation between religious community staffing the school and the building planning committee in regard to school and convent facilities.

(   ) 24. provides adequate furnishings and utilities and arranges for their maintenance and repairs.

(   ) 25. cooperates with the major superior and community supervisor of the teaching sisters staffing the school.

(   ) 26. conforms to the salary scale of the diocese in paying adequate salaries to religious and lay teachers.

(   ) 27.

(   ) 28.

EVALUATIONS

(   ) *a. How effectively does the pastor perform his obligations toward the school?*

(   ) *b. To what extent does the pastor cooperate with the principal and staff members to provide a high quality instructional program in the school?*

(   ) *c. How extensive is the rapport between the pastor and the religious community conducting the school?*

COMMENTS

5. The Principal and Administrative Assistants

A. *Preparation and Qualifications*

CHECKLIST

The principal and administrative assistants:

( ) 1. have a liberal education.

( ) 2. have administrative certification.

( ) 3. have extensive professional preparation.

( ) 4. have successful classroom experience.

( ) 5. have a thorough knowledge of the philosophy of Catholic education.

( ) 6. organize an educational program that promotes our American way of life based on Christian social principles.

( ) 7. are conversant with the educational needs of the community.

( ) 8. provide special educational opportunities and facilities.

( ) 9. keep informed of current trends in philosophy, research and practices in elementary education.

( ) 10. hold membership in professional organizations.

( ) 11. attend meetings of professional organizations.

( ) 12. are qualified to initiate, conduct, and utilize the results of experimentation and research.

( ) 13. encourage initiative and research on part of the staff.

( ) 14.

( ) 15.

EVALUATIONS

( ) *a. How adequate is the professional preparation of the administrative staff?*

( ) *b. How extensive is the educational experience of the administrative staff?*

( ) *c. How adequately are the principles of Catholic philosophy implemented in administrative practices?*

COMMENTS

B. *Duties and Functions*

The following functions are usually considered the responsibility of the principal but their performance may be delegated to others. Evaluate this area on the basis of performance of functions by the proper persons, regardless of position in administration.

CHECKLIST

The principal:

( ) 1. has delegated authority as the responsible educational head of the school.

( ) 2. is responsible for those delegated for the articulation and continuity of all aspects of the school program, both within the grades and between grades.

( ) 3. schedules adequate time for supervision and improvement of instruction.

( ) 4. encourages and actively assists teachers in the organization and implementation of their duties.

( ) 5. keeps the lines of communication open and provides all staff members with definite information regarding their duties and responsibilities.

( ) 6. cooperates with the regulations of the diocesan school board.

( ) 7. interprets diocesan office policies to the staff.

( ) 8. works in conjunction with the diocesan office on curriculum studies.

( ) 9. directs the public relations program in cooperation with the pastor and superintendent.

( ) 10. cooperates with public school officials.

( ) 11. makes an equitable division of workload of staff members.

( ) 12. provides opportunities for staff members to share in the administrative duties of the school.

( ) 13. acts as counselor and pedagogical guide to teachers.

( ) 14. uses a friendly, understanding, objective and ethical approach in discussing teacher problems.

( ) 15. provides a program of orientation for new teachers so that they may begin their work effectively.

( ) 16. provides opportunities for in-service education for teachers.

( ) 17. encourages and guides teachers in the use of new techniques and practices.

( ) 18. arranges for inter-class or inter-school visitation.

( ) 19. arranges for attendance at workshops and conferences, and for reports on these to all members of the staff.

( ) 20. provides a professional library and actively promotes its use.

( ) 21. strives to encourage a professional attitude toward teaching and administration.

( ) 22. provides for staff meetings at regular intervals.

( ) 23. provides up-to-date teaching materials and multi-sensory aids and assumes responsibility for their care and use.

( ) 24. provides class schedules, attendance data, reports, and all administrative forms in sufficient time to warrant their proper use.

( ) 25. formulates plans in cooperation with staff for the improvement of the educational program.

( ) 26. makes regular inspection of plant facilities.

( ) 27. provides a program of safety education.

( ) 28. directs the supervision and control of student activities.

( ) 29. studies the grouping of students for instructional purposes.

( ) 30. recommends the selection of staff members.

( ) 31. evaluates periodically the educational program to determine areas of strengths and weaknesses.

( ) 32. cooperates with home and school organizations and with local public schools to improve the school services to the parish and the community.

( ) 33. reviews and approves news releases.

( ) 34. resists pressures to divert school time to activities of minor educational significance.

( ) 35. safeguards the professional reputation of the staff.

( ) 36. alerts staff to the obligation to safeguard family and student reputation.

( ) 37. keeps informed of national and international cultural trends and anticipates the probable impact of these forces on Catholic education.

( ) 38. recognizes responsibility for leadership in adjusting to social and cultural change.

( ) 39. is committed both personally and professionally to improvement of Catholic education.

( ) 40. provides for articulation between elementary and secondary schools.

( ) 41.

( ) 42.

(Continued on next page)

Duties and Functions (Continued from previous page)

The principal:

EVALUATIONS

(   ) *a. How effectively do the principal and assistants perform their duties?*
(   ) *b. How effectively does the principal provide opportunities for staff members to participate in administration?*
(   ) *c. How cooperatively do all members of the staff participate in staff meetings?*
(   ) *d. How effective are staff meetings?*
(   ) *e. To what extent are opportunities provided for in-service education?*

COMMENTS

C. INSTRUCTIONAL STAFF

1. Selection of Staff Members

CHECKLIST

( ) 1. Qualifications and assignments of religious teachers are the responsibility of the Religious Community staffing the school.

( ) 2. Selection of lay teachers is a cooperative process involving pastor, principal, and diocesan school office.

( ) 3. Selection of all teachers is based on state and diocesan requirements.

( ) 4. Teaching experience, both quantitative and qualitative, of each prospective teacher is considered.

( ) 5. Examination of the college transcript of each applicant is required.

( ) 6. Recommendations from reliable sources are sought and confidentially considered.

( ) 7. Each prospective lay member of the instructional staff is granted a personal interview by pastor and principal and/or diocesan personnel.

( ) 8. The prospective teacher is observed in a teaching situation, when this is possible.

( ) 9.

( ) 10.

EVALUATIONS

( ) *a. How satisfactory are the methods used in the selection of professional staff members?*

( ) *b. How successful has the present administration been in selecting competent staff members?*

COMMENTS

2. Experience and Length of Service—(Male) (Female)

Indicate below the experience of classroom teachers.

No. of Yrs. of Experience	Length of Service in This School						Experience in Other Catholic Schools						Teaching Experience in Public School						Total School Experience					
	Number						Number						Number						Number					
	Rel.		Lay		%		Rel.		Lay		%		Rel.		Lay		%		Rel.		Lay		%	
	M	F	M	F			M	F	M	F			M	F	M	F			M	F	M	F		
25 or more																								
20 – 24																								
15 – 19																								
10 – 14																								
5 – 9																								
1 – 4																								
Less than 1																								
TOTAL					100						100						100						100	

EVALUATIONS

( ) *a. How satisfactory is the total amount of experience of teachers?*

( ) *b. How satisfactory is the length of service of teachers in this school?*

COMMENTS

3. Staff Improvement

CHECKLIST

Members of the school staff:

( ) 1. utilize studies of students and community.

( ) 2. study and discuss problems relating to: (check)

_____ philosophy and objectives.
_____ state requirements.
_____ community and community resources.
_____ social conditions of parish and community.
_____ professional ethics.
_____ curriculum development.
_____ individual differences.
_____ guidance services of school.
_____ instructional materials services.
_____ student activity program.
_____ methods of teaching.
_____ techniques of evaluation.
_____ in-service education.
_____ special education.
_____ others.

_____

_____

( ) 3. plan and participate in faculty meetings.

( ) 4. make use of faculty meetings for school and staff improvement.

( ) 5. seek professional assistance from outside sources when necessary or desirable.

( ) 6. make use of professional publications.

( ) 7. seek ways of increasing their knowledge in specialization of subject areas.

( ) 8. add to their formal education through courses or other recognized means.

( ) 9. are given opportunities to participate in professional activities both within and without the diocese at parish expense.

( ) 10. are provided diocesan supported in-service education programs.

( ) 11.

( ) 12.

EVALUATIONS

( ) *a. To what extent are appropriate study materials available to staff members?*

( ) *b. How extensive is the study of school problems by the staff?*

( ) *c. To what extent are opportunities provided for in-service professional growth?*

COMMENTS

4. Teaching Load Policy

CHECKLIST

( ) 1. Extra class responsibilities are distributed equitably among all members of the staff.

( ) 2. The minimum school 'day for staff members conforms to diocesan policies.

( ) 3. The maximum teaching time per day is in accordance with diocesan regulations.

( ) 4. The maximum pupil enrollment per teacher is in accordance with diocesan regulations.

( ) 5. Adjustments are made in the teaching schedule of primary, intermediate and upper grade coordinators, master teachers, or advisors, to permit supervisory work.

( ) 6. Special schedules are provided for teachers of double grades.

( ) 7. Class schedules are arranged to accommodate teachers of special subjects, team teaching, etc.

SUPPLEMENTARY DATA

(Complete table)

DISTRIBUTION OF CLASSES BY SIZE		
	Number of Classes	Per cent of Total Classes
Above 50		
46 – 50		
41 – 45		
36 – 40		
31 – 35		
26 – 30		
21 – 25		
16 – 20		
11 – 15		
Below 11		
Total		

SUPPLEMENTARY DATA

Describe in detail the duties of a coordinator, master teacher, or advisor.

EVALUATIONS

( ) *a. How satisfactory is the teaching-load policy?*

( ) *b. How adequate is the time allotted for teaching?*

( ) *c. How satisfactory are the provisions for teachers of double grades?*

COMMENTS

5. Tenure, Leave of Absence, Dismissals, and Retirement Provisions (Lay Teachers)

CHECKLIST

(   ) 1. A successful probationary period is required before tenure is granted to lay teachers.

(   ) 2. A formal warning of dismissal is given a teacher, if guidance has failed.

(   ) 3. There is no deduction in salary when absence for professional reasons is approved by the principal and diocesan school policy.

(   ) 4. Diocesan policy, relative to leave of absence, is observed.

(   ) 5. A retirement plan is provided.

(   ) 6. Contracts are used in the employment of lay teachers.

(   ) 7.

(   ) 8.

SUPPLEMENTARY DATA

1. Describe any fringe benefits provided for staff members, indicating specific staff members included.
2. Attach a copy of any contract form.

EVALUATIONS

(   ) a. *How adequate are provisions for tenure of professional staff members?*

(   ) b. *How adequate are provisions for leave of absence?*

(   ) c. *How adequate are the retirement plans?*

COMMENTS

D. NONINSTRUCTIONAL STAFF

1. Secretarial

CHECKLIST

( ) 1. A professionally competent secretary is provided for the principal.

( ) 2. Selection of a secretary is made after careful study of qualifications for the position.

( ) 3. A just salary is provided.

( ) 4. Provision for leave of absence is made.

( ) 5. Tenure is assured under specified conditions.

( ) 6. An employee is given adequate advice and help before warning of dismissal is issued.

( ) 7.

( ) 8.

SUPPLEMENTARY DATA

1. Describe the provisions for retirement.
2. Describe the provisions for a leave of absence.

EVALUATIONS

( ) *a. How satisfactorily do secretaries perform duties?*

( ) *b. How adequate is secretarial help?*

( ) *c. How adequate are the salaries?*

COMMENTS

2. Custodial and Maintenance Staff

CHECKLIST

(   ) 1. Staff members are employed on the basis of their competence for the position.

(   ) 2. Direction of work is channeled through pastor, principal, or delegate.

(   ) 3. Custodians have adequate training in the care and use of equipment.

(   ) 4. Engineers hold a license from an authoritative agency.

(   ) 5. The principal is consulted in the employment of custodial personnel.

(   ) 6. The work-load is confined to definite, assigned areas.

(   ) 7. The salary provides a just, living wage.

(   ) 8. The work-day (and week) is a reasonable one.

(   ) 9. Custodians understand the implications for health and safety in their work.

(   ) 10. School is maintained in a clean and sanitary condition.

(   ) 11. Equipment provided is modern and suitable.

(   ) 12. Equipment and supplies are used efficiently and economically.

(   ) 13. Provisions for tenure and retirement are made.

(   ) 14. Tenure is dependent on satisfactory work.

(   ) 15. The engineer is on the school premises during all class hours.

(   ) 16. Dismissal of an employee is preceded by a formal warning.

(   ) 17.

(   ) 18.

EVALUATIONS

(   ) a. *How satisfactory are the methods used in selecting custodial and maintenance staff?*

(   ) b. *How numerically adequate is the custodial staff?*

(   ) c. *How well does the salary scale for custodial staff members conform to social justice?*

(   ) d. *How well do members of the custodial staff perform assigned duties?*

COMMENTS

3. Health and Medical Staff

CHECKLIST

( ) 1. A trained nurse is available during school hours.

( ) 2. Office files include a list of trained nurses available for volunteer service.

( ) 3. A physician is available on call during school hours.

( ) 4. Teachers are qualified to administer first aid.

( ) 5. An emergency release card is on file in the principal's office.

( ) 6. Health services of the local district are made available through the school.

( ) 7. Hearing and vision tests are given periodically.

( ) 8. Dental and physical examinations are given periodically.

( ) 9.

( ) 10.

SUPPLEMENTARY DATA

1. Attach a copy of emergency release card.
2. Attach a copy of health card.

EVALUATIONS

( ) *a. How adequate are the health services of the school?*

( ) *b. How adequately is the school able to administer first aid?*

( ) *c. How well does the school utilize available local health services?*

COMMENTS

II. Organization and Management

A. PUPIL ACCOUNTING

CHECKLIST

(   ) 1. Current and permanent records of all students are kept on file.

(   ) 2. Permanent records give data and reasons for withdrawal.

(   ) 3. Health sections of record give information about accidents.

(   ) 4. Parish census data are available in order to plan for future educational needs.

(   ) 5. An accurate daily attendance record is kept.

(   ) 6. Absentee and tardiness forms are provided for teachers.

(   ) 7. Attendance is checked at the beginning of morning and afternoon sessions.

(   ) 8. Excused absence forms are used.

(   ) 9. Written excuse from parent or guardian is requested upon return to class after absence.

(   ) 10. Service of attendance officer is available.

(   ) 11.

(   ) 12.

SUPPLEMENTARY DATA *(Attach copies of all forms used in pupil accounting)*

EVALUATIONS

(   ) *a. To what extent are the forms used in pupil accounting satisfactory?*

(   ) *b. To what extent are pupil accounting methods effective?*

COMMENTS

B. REPORTS TO PARENTS

CHECKLIST

(   ) 1. Progress reports of students are issued periodically to parents.

(   ) 2. Material of report card is definite in content and easily interpreted.

(   ) 3. Parent-teacher conferences are held periodically.

(   ) 4. Parents, teachers, and counselors confer on specific problems.

(   ) 5.

(   ) 6.

SUPPLEMENTARY DATA

1. Attach a copy of report forms to parents.
2. Attach form used for record of parent-teacher conference.

EVALUATIONS

(   ) *a. How satisfactory are the forms used to report student progress to parents?*

(   ) *b. How satisfactory are the methods for reporting student progress?*

(   ) *c. How satisfactory are arrangements for parent-teacher conferences?*

COMMENTS

C. SCHOOL FINANCE

Attach a statement describing the manner in which this school is financed.

D. SCHOOL SCHEDULE

CHECKLIST

( ) 1. Forms are developed which simplify schedule making.

( ) 2. Class schedules are on file in the office.

( ) 3. Schedules are in operation on the opening day of school.

( ) 4. Schedule follows diocesan time allotment.

( ) 5. Consideration is given to flexibility in programming.

( ) 6. A form is prepared showing room number, capacity in each room, and periods in which room is in use.

( ) 7. Homeroom lists of students are made available to each teacher.

( ) 8. Class sizes are kept within limits determined by the diocesan school office.

( ) 9. The schedule form provides information on location of teachers and students during class and all activities.

( ) 10.

( ) 11.

EVALUATIONS

( ) a. *How satisfactory are the forms used in development of class schedules?*

( ) b. *How satisfactory is the filing system for organizational materials?*

( ) c. *How satisfactory is the school schedule to meet student needs?*

E. MAINTENANCE AND OPERATION OF PLANT

CHECKLIST

( ) 1. Regular and systematic inspection of all school property provides checks on conditions affecting safety and health of school personnel.

( ) 2. Repairs and improvements, except those requiring immediate attention, are made when school is not in session.

( ) 3. Necessary repairs are made promptly.

( ) 4. Regular maintenance of building is planned so as not to interrupt daily program.

( ) 5. Fire regulations are conscientiously observed.

( ) 6. Fire drills for all school personnel are executed in accordance with local fire regulations, at least once a month.

( ) 7. Security or civil defense drills for all school personnel are held as required by proper authorities.

( ) 8. Student traffic throughout the school plant is planned and directed for the best interests of all concerned.

( ) 9. Unsafe conditions and hazardous practices are reported to proper authority.

( ) 10. Reports of unsafe conditions and hazardous practices receive immediate attention.

( ) 11.

( ) 12.

EVALUATIONS

( ) a. *To what extent are building inspection procedures adequate?*

( ) b. *How satisfactory are repairs and maintenance of building?*

( ) c. *To what extent is provision made for the safety of school personnel?*

COMMENTS

F. LUNCHROOM, DINING ROOMS, AND KITCHEN

The school administration is responsible for lunchroom activities regardless of the personnel operating such services.

CHECKLIST

(   ) 1. Satisfactory lunch service is available to students and staff.

(   ) 2. Lunch service personnel is adequate for the program.

(   ) 3. Food served is of satisfactory quality and quantity.

(   ) 4. Balanced, appetizing meals are served at moderate cost.

(   ) 5. Attention is given to table etiquette.

(   ) 6. A congenial atmosphere is maintained during lunch period.

(   ) 7. Lunch service to needy children is available without cost.

(   ) 8. Lunchroom is available to students who bring their own lunch.

(   ) 9. School utilizes available aid for lunch program where deemed feasible.

(   ) 10.

(   ) 11.

SUPPLEMENTARY DATA

1. Period(s) for lunch in minutes...——————

2. Number of students served daily in lunchroom...——————

EVALUATIONS

(   ) *a. How satisfactory are the meals served in the lunch program?*

(   ) *b. How satisfactory is the supervision of the lunchroom and services?*

(   ) *c. To what extent does the lunchroom offer opportunities for social education?*

COMMENTS

G. TRANSPORTATION OF STUDENTS

CHECKLIST

(   )   1. Every precaution is taken to ensure that the school bus service is safe.

(   )   2. School buses are owned or leased by the parish or diocese.

(   )   3. Adequate insurance coverage is maintained.

(   )   4. Bus schedules and routes are planned to provide efficient and economical service.

(   )   5. Drills are held regularly to teach children to evacuate the bus by means of the emergency door.

(   )   6. Students are instructed in the rules of courteous and safe bus riding.

(   )   7. Bus drivers meet standard requirements of character, health, driving experience, and knowledge of traffic regulations.

(   )   8. Bus drivers cooperate with school personnel.

(   )   9. School bus accidents are reported promptly and investigated thoroughly.

(   ) 10.

(   ) 11.

SUPPLEMENTARY DATA

1. Number of students using school bus transportation.._____

2. Per cent of students transported by bus.._____

3. Attach a copy of the bus schedule in operation.

4. Attach a copy of bus financing procedure.

EVALUATIONS

(   ) *a. How efficient is the school bus transportation service?*

(   ) *b. How well do bus drivers meet requirements?*

(   ) *c. How safely conducted is the bus transportation service?*

COMMENTS

III. Community Relations

A. PROVIDING INFORMATION

CHECKLIST

The school furnishes parishioners and civic community with information concerning:

(   )   1. the philosophy and objectives of the school.

(   )   2. the curriculum of the school.

(   )   3. the personnel and organization of the school staff.

(   )   4. the school plant and equipment.

(   )   5. the financial cost of the educational program.

(   )   6. the policies of the school pertaining to attendance, reports, promotion, conduct, and dress.

(   )   7. accomplishments of students.

(   )   8. regulations pertaining to parent-teacher conferences.

(   )   9. scheduled activities of the school.

(   )   10. membership in community organizations.

(   )   11.

(   )   12.

EVALUATIONS

(   )   *a. How adequately are the members of the parish informed about the school?*

(   )   *b. How adequately is the civic community informed about the school?*

COMMENTS

B. COMMUNITY SERVICES

CHECKLIST

(   )   1. The staff is active in community organizations such as parish activities, service clubs, youth organizations, safety organizations and civil defense.

(   )   2. The building is available to the public for educational and recreational activities, provided they do not interfere with the school program.

(   )   3. These facilities are available for community use: (Check those in operation)

    _____ auditorium

    _____ classrooms

    _____ all-purpose room

    _____ gymnasium

    _____ play areas

    _____ library

    _____ cafeteria

    _____ others

(   )   4.

(   )   5.

EVALUATIONS

(   )   *a. To what extent are school buildings and facilities made available and used for parish activities?*

(   )   *b. To what extent are school buildings and facilities used for community service?*

COMMENTS

C. PROCEDURES

The school has a planned public relations program.

CHECKLIST

(　　) 1. The principal establishes and maintains good public relations with newspaper editors, reporters, radio and TV personnel.

(　　) 2. A staff member is appointed in charge of all news items pertaining to the achievements of the students and staff and the progress of the school program.

(　　) 3. The school promotes the well-being of its youth and the community by cooperation with other agencies.

(　　) 4. Parents are kept informed about the school and its policies through school bulletins and planned meetings.

(　　) 5. Home and school associations cooperate in working for the educational welfare of youth and in developing better mutual understanding between teachers and parents.

(　　) 6. Social and educational activities are used to promote good public relations between the school and the community.

(　　) 7. The school sponsors the following: (check)
_____ education week
_____ book week
_____ parent conferences
_____ home and school association meetings
_____ guest speakers
_____ demonstration lessons
_____ exhibits
_____ other

(　　) 8. The school has an open-house session where visitors may observe the educational procedures of the staff and students.

(　　) 9. School and parish bulletins interpret the school and its purposes to the community.

(　　) 10.

(　　) 11.

EVALUATIONS

(　　) a. *How well does the school use all available means to promote better school and community relations?*

(　　) b. *How effective is the Home and School Association in developing mutual understanding between teachers and parents?*

(　　) c. *How effective is the Home and School Association in developing mutual understanding between the school and the public?*

(　　) d. *How well do parishioners and the civic community understand the policies of the school and support its activities?*

COMMENTS

V. Special Characteristics of Administration and Staff

1. What are the outstanding characteristics of the administration and staff?

    a.

    b.

    c.

2. In what areas have administration and staff a definite need of improvement?

    a.

    b.

    c.

3. What specific improvements have been made by administration and staff within the last three years?

    a.

    b.

    c.

4. What improvements are currently being made or planned for the immediate future?

    a.

    b.

    c.

5. What studies have the administration and staff made in an effort to solve their problems?

    a.

    b.

    c.

VI. General Evaluations of Administration and Staff

(   ) a. *To what extent are policies and procedures of the administration and staff consistent with the philosophy and objectives as outlined in Section B?*

(   ) b. *How adequately does the administration and staff meet the needs of the students as stated in Section C?*

(   ) c. *How adequately does the administration and staff recognize their problems and seek their solutions?*

Formulated and Edited by the Criteria Committee, Elementary School
Department of The National Catholic Educational Association

Individual Staff Member

This "K" Blank is to be filled out by each member of the school personnel engaged in administration (full or part time), classroom teaching, or specialized services of a professional nature directly associated with the school making the self-evaluation.

The "K" Blank indicates specific assignments, professional preparation, experience, and in-service work of each staff member.

School_____ Position_____

Name_____ Grade_____ Section_____

Diocese_____ City and State _____ Date_____

If part time, indicate hours per week given to this school _____

DAILY SCHEDULE

Indicate below your regularly assigned duties.

TIME SPAN	SUBJECT	GRADE	RM. N.	NUMBER STUDENTS	M.	T.	W.	TH.	F.

I. Preparation

A. Secondary School Attendance

Name of School	City and State	Date of Attendance

B. College and University Attendance

Name of College	State	Dates of Attendance	Degree Granted	Date

C. Teaching Experience (List chronologically, attach typed sheet if necessary.)

Position	School	City and State	Dates	Number of Years

D. Background Experience Other Than Teaching

Position	Place	Dates	Number of Years

E. Academic Preparation (Exclusive of Professional Education Courses)

Professional Education Courses

Subject	Semester hrs. credit		Course Title	Semester hrs. credit	
	Undergrad.	Grad.		Undergrad.	Grad.

F. In-service Preparation (List here services received within the past five years in Community Workshops, Diocesan Workshops, Seminars, and other educational groups which added to your professional preparation but for which no academic credit was received.) Attach typed sheet, if necessary.

Subject Area	Sponsor of Work	Dates

G. Describe below any system of INTERNSHIP aiding professional advancement in which you have participated.

II. Professional Participation

A. Indicate below the names of national or regional professional associations of which you are a member. (e.g., National Catholic Educational Association, National Council Teachers of English, etc.)

1. _____
2. _____
3. _____
4. _____

B. List below any national, state, community or diocesan research committees of which you are a member or have served with during the past ten years.

1. _____
2. _____
3. _____
4. _____

C. List below the names and dates of attendance at national, regional, community or diocesan conventions or workshops you have attended during the past five years. Attach typed sheet, if necessary.

	Organization	City	Dates
1.	_____	_____	_____
2.	_____	_____	_____
3.	_____	_____	_____
4.	_____	_____	_____

D. List below any books or articles you have written, addresses or other professional contributions you have made during the past ten years. Attach additional sheet, if necessary.

E. List below professional books, journals, articles and other materials allied to your professional work which you read regularly.

Formulated and Edited by the Criteria Committee, Elementary School
Department of The National Catholic Educational Association

Statistical Summary of Evaluation

The "Statistical Summary," SECTION X, provides the necessary forms on which the school may summarize statistically all data in the Areas of the Criteria that have been evaluated by the school. Numerical ratings of the evaluation items are transferred to their appropriate place on these forms. The evaluation ratings are then totaled, and this total is divided by the number of evaluation items on which the total is based in order to obtain the average rating for a particular section. (Note that any items marked "MN" or "N" are not included in the total.) This average rating is then transferred to the appropriate bar in the "Graphic Summary," SECTION Y.

Since the evaluations in each major division, indicated by Roman numerals, of SECTIONS D, E, F, G, H, I, and J are averaged, an appropriate column has been added to the statistical summary forms for these sections. Note that the average of the TOTALS in the lower right-hand corner of each form is based upon the *total of the evaluations* divided by the *total of the divisors*. *It is not an average of the numbers* appearing in the "average" column.

Sections X and Y are intended to provide the staff a means for making a careful analysis in summary forms of any section of the CRITERIA.

Name of School	(Arch)Diocese
Address	City	State
Date of Evaluation	Evaluation Coordinator

D. Curriculum

DIVISION	TITLE OF DIVISION	PAGE	EVALUATIONS					DIVISOR*	TOTAL	AVERAGE**
I	Organization		a	b	c	d	————→	4		
II	Curriculum Development Procedures		a	b	c	d	————→	4		
III A	Extent of Subject Offerings		a	b	c		————→			
III B	General Characteristics of Curriculum		a	b	c	d	————→	18		
III C	Instructional Activities		a	b	c	d	e	f			
III D	Methods of Evaluation		a	b	c	d	e	→			
IV	General Outcomes		a	b			————————→	2		
VI	General Evaluation		a	b	c		————————→	3		
	Total							31		

. * Number of evaluations minus number marked MN or N.
** Transfer to Section Y—appropriate area.

D-1. Art

DIVISION	TITLE OF DIVISION	PAGE	EVALUATIONS							DIVISOR*	TOTAL
I	Organization		a	b	c	d	————→			4	
II	Nature of Offerings		a	b	c	d	e	——→		5	
III	Physical Facilities		a	b	c	d	————→			4	
IV A	Direction of Learning Instructional Staff		a	b	c	————————→				3	
IV B	Instructional Activities		a	b	c	————————→				3	
IV C	Instructional Materials		a	b	————————————→					2	
IV D	Methods of Evaluation		a	b	————————————→					2	
V	Outcomes		a	b	c	d	e	f	g	7	
VII	General Evaluation of Instruction of Art		a	b	c	————————→				3	
	Total									33	
	Average**										

* Number of evaluations minus number marked MN or N.
** Transfer to Section Y—appropriate area.

D-2. English Language Arts

Division	Title of Division	Page	Evaluations							Divisor*	Total
I	Organization		*a*	*b*	———————————→					2	
II	Nature of Offerings		*a*	*b*	*c*	*d*	*e*	*f*	*g*	13	
			h	*i*	*j*	*k*	*l*	*m*	——→		
III	Physical Facilities		*a*	*b*	*c*	————————→				3	
IV A	Instructional Staff		*a*	*b*	*c*	*d*	———→			4	
IV B	Instructional Activities		*a*	*b*	*c*	*d*	———→			4	
IV C	Instructional Materials		*a*	*b*	*c*	————→				3	
IV D	Methods of Evaluation		*a*	*b*	*c*	*d*	———→			4	
V	Outcomes		*a*	*b*	*c*	*d*	*e*	*f*	*g*	11	
			h	*i*	*j*	*k*	———→				
VII	General Evaluation of Instruction in English Language Arts		*a*	*b*	*c*	————→				3	

* Number of evaluations minus number marked MN or N.
** Transfer to Section Y—appropriate area.

Total	47
Average**	

D-3. Foreign Languages

Division	Title of Division	Page	Evaluations					Divisor*	Total
I	Organization		*a*	*b*	*c*	———→		3	
II	Nature of Offerings		*a*	*b*	*c*	*d*	——→	4	
III	Physical Facilities		*a*	*b*	————→			2	
IV A	Instructional Staff		*a*	*b*	*c*	*d*	——→	4	
IV B	Instructional Activities		*a*	*b*	*c*	*d*	*e*	5	
IV C	Instructional Materials		*a*	*b*	*c*	*d*	*e*	5	
IV D	Methods of Evaluation		*a*	*b*	*c*	*d*	——→	4	
V	Outcomes		*a*	*b*	*c*	*d*	——→	4	
VII	General Evaluation of Instruction in Foreign Language		*a*	*b*	*c*	————→		3	

* Number of evaluations minus number marked MN or N.
** Transfer to Section Y—appropriate area.

Total	34
Average**	

D-4. Geography

DIVISION	TITLE OF DIVISION	PAGE	EVALUATIONS							DIVISOR*	TOTAL
I	Organization		*a*	*b*	*c*	*d*	*e*	⟶		5	
II	Nature of Offerings		*a*	*b*	*c*	*d*	*e*	⟶		5	
III	Physical Facilities		*a*	*b*	*c*	⟶				3	
IV A	Instructional Staff		*a*	*b*	*c*	⟶				3	
IV B	Instructional Activities		*a*	*b*	*c*	*d*	⟶			4	
IV C	Instructional Materials		*a*	*b*	*c*	*d*	*e*	⟶		5	
IV D	Methods of Evaluation		*a*	*b*	*c*	*d*	*e*	⟶		5	
V	Outcomes		*a*	*b*	*c*	*d*	*e*	*f*	*g*	8	
			h	⟶							
VII	General Evaluation of Instruction in Geography		*a*	*b*	*c*	⟶				3	

* Number of evaluations minus number marked MN or N.
** Transfer to Section Y—appropriate area.

Total	41
Average**	

D-5. Health and Physical Education

DIVISION	TITLE OF DIVISION	PAGE	EVALUATIONS								DIVISOR*	TOTAL
I	Organization		a	b	c	d	e	⟶			5	
II	Nature of Offerings		a	b	c	d	e	f	⟶		6	
III	Physical Facilities		a	b	c	d	e	⟶			5	
IV	Direction of Learning		⟶									
IV A	Instructional Staff		a	b	c	d	⟶				4	
IV B	Instructional Activities		a	b	c	d	e	f	⟶		6	
IV C	Instructional Materials		a	b	c	d	e	⟶			5	
IV D	Methods of Evaluation		a	b	c	⟶					3	
V	Outcomes		a	b	c	d	e	f	g		9	
			h	i	⟶							
VII	General Evaluation of Health and Physical Education		a	b	c	d	⟶				4	

* Number of evaluations minus number marked MN or N.
** Transfer to Section Y—appropriate area.

Total	47	
Average**		

D-6. History

Division	Title of Division	Page	Evaluations								Divisor*	Total
I	Organization		a	b	c	d					4	
II	Nature of Offerings		a	b	c	d					4	
III	Physical Facilities		a	b							2	
IV A	Instructional Staff		a	b	c						3	
IV B	Instructional Activities		a	b	c						3	
IV C	Instructional Materials		a	b							2	
IV D	Method of Evaluation		a	b	c	d					4	
V	Outcomes		a	b	c	d	e	f	g		8	
			h									
VII	General Evaluation of Instruction in History		a	b	c						3	

* Number of evaluations minus number marked MN or N.
** Transfer to Section Y—appropriate area.

Total	33	
Average**		

D-7. Mathematics

Division	Title of Division	Page	Evaluations								Divisor*	Total
I	Organization		a	b	c	d	e				5	
II	Nature of Offerings		a	b	c	d	e				5	
III	Physical Facilities		a	b	c						3	
IV A	Instructional Staff		a	b	c						3	
IV B	Instructional Activities		a	b	c	d					4	
IV C	Instructional Materials		a	b	c						3	
IV D	Methods of Evaluation		a	b	c						3	
V	Outcomes		a	b	c	d	e	f	g		7	
VII	General Evaluation of Instruction in Mathematics		a	b	c						3	

* Number of evaluations minus number marked MN or N.
** Transfer to Section Y—appropriate area.

Total	36	
Average**		

D-8. Music

Division	Title of Division	Page	Evaluations									Divisor*	Total
I	Organization		*a*	*b*	*c*	*d*	⟶					4	
II	Nature of Offerings		*a*	*b*	*c*	*d*	*e*	⟶				5	
III	Physical Facilities		*a*	*b*	⟶							2	
IV A	Instructional Staff		*a*	*b*	*c*	⟶						3	
IV B	Instructional Activities		*a*	*b*	*c*	*d*	⟶					4	
IV C	Instructional Materials		*a*	*b*	*c*	⟶						3	
IV D	Methods of Evaluation		*a*	*b*	⟶							2	
V	Outcomes		*a*	*b*	*c*	*d*	*e*	*f*	*g*			9	
			h	*i*	⟶								
VII	General Evaluation of Instruction in Music		*a*	*b*	*c*	⟶						3	

* Number of evaluations minus number marked MN or N.
** Transfer to Section Y—appropriate area.

Total	35
Average**	

D-9. Religion

Division	Title of Division	Page	Evaluations									Divisor*	Total
I	Organization		*a*	*b*	*c*	*d*	*e*	*f*	*g*			7	
II	Nature of Offerings		*a*	*b*	*c*	*d*	*e*	⟶				5	
III	Physical Facilities		*a*	*b*	*c*	⟶						3	
IV A	Instructional Staff		*a*	*b*	*c*	*d*	*e*	⟶				5	
IV B	Instructional Activities		*a*	*b*	*c*	*d*	*e*	⟶				5	
IV C	Instructional Materials		*a*	*b*	*c*	*d*	⟶					4	
IV D	Methods of Evaluation		*a*	*b*	*c*	*d*	*e*	⟶				5	
V	Outcomes		*a*	*b*	*c*	*d*	*e*	*f*	*g*			14	
			h	*i*	*j*	*k*	*l*	*m*	*n*				
VII	General Evaluation of Instruction in Religion		*a*	*b*	*c*	*d*	⟶					4	

* Number of evaluations minus number marked MN or N.
** Transfer to Section Y—appropriate area.

Total	52
Average**	

D-10. Science

Division	Title of Division	Page	Evaluations							Divisor*	Total
I	Organization		a	b	c	d	e	⟶		5	
II	Nature of Offerings		a	b	⟶					2	
III	Physical Facilities		a	b	c	d	e	f	⟶	6	
IV A	Instructional Staff		a	b	c	d	⟶			4	
IV B	Instructional Activities		a	b	c	d	e	⟶		5	
IV C	Instructional Materials		a	b	c	d	⟶			4	
IV D	Methods of Evaluation		a	b	c	d	⟶			4	
V	Outcomes		a	b	c	d	e	f	g	10	
			h	i	j	⟶					
VII	General Evaluation of Instruction in Science		a	b	c	⟶				3	

* Number of evaluations minus number marked MN or N.
** Transfer to Section Y—appropriate area.

Total	43	
Average**		

E. Student Activity Program

Division	Title of Division	Page	Evaluations						Divisor*	Total	Average**
I A	General Organization of the Program		a	b	c	d	⟶		7		
I B	General Nature of the Program		a	b	c	⟶					
II	Service Activities		a	b	⟶				2		
III	Creative Activities		a	b	c	d	⟶		4		
IV	Physical Activities		a	b	c	d	e	f	6		
VI	General Evaluation of the Student Activity Program		a	b	c	⟶			3		▨

* Number of evaluations minus number marked MN or N.
** Transfer to Section Y—appropriate area.

Total	22

F. Instructional Materials Services—Library and Multi-Sensory Aids

Division	Title of Division	Page	Evaluations						Divisor*	Total	Average**
I. Instructional Materials Staff											
I A	Numerical Adequacy		a	b	c	d	e	f			
I B	General Qualifications		a	b	c	d	⟶		18		
I C	Responsibilities		a	b	c	d	⟶				
I D	Services		a	b	c	d	⟶				
II. Organization and Management											
II A	Financial Provisions		a	b	c	d	⟶				
II B	Selection of Materials and Equipment		a	b	c	d	⟶				
II C	Classifying, Cataloging, and Processing of Materials		a	b	c	d	e	⟶	17		
II D	Accessibility of Instructional Materials Services		a	b	⟶						
II E	Care and Maintenance of Materials and Equipment		a	b	⟶						
III. Materials											
III-A-1	Printed Materials Books		a	b	c	d	e	f			
			g	h	i	j	k	l			
			m	⟶							
III-A-2	Periodicals and Newspapers		a	b	⟶				29		
III-A-3	Vertical File Materials and Pamphlets		a	b	c	⟶					
III B	Nonprint Materials		a	b	c	d	e	f			
			g	h	i	j	k	⟶			
IV. Physical Facilities											
IV A	Quarters		a	b	c	d	⟶				
IV B	Furnishings and Fixed Equipment		a	b	⟶				9		
IV C	Multi-Sensory Equipment and facilities		a	b	c	⟶					
VI. General Evaluation of Instructional Materials Services			a	b	c	d	⟶		4		░░░

* Number of evaluations minus number marked MN or N.
** Transfer to Section Y—appropriate area.

Total		77	

G. Guidance Services

Division	Title of Division	Page	Evaluations			Divisor*	Total	Average**
I	General Organization and Nature		a	b	⟶	2		
II	Guidance Staff		a	b	⟶	2		
III-A-1	Guidance Services Sources of Information about Students		a	b	⟶			
III-A-2	Maintenance and Use of Information		a	b	⟶	9		
III B	Guidance of Students		a	b	c			
III C	Placement Services		a	b	⟶			
V	General Evaluation of Guidance Services		a	b	c	3		

* Number of evaluations minus number marked MN or N.
** Transfer to Section Y—appropriate area.

Total   16

H. Health and Safety Services

Division	Title of Division	Page	Evaluations						Divisor*	Total	Average**
I	General Nature and Organization		a	b	c	d	e	f	7		
			g	⟶							
II	School Health and Safety Services										
II A	Health Appraisal and Records		a	b	c	⟶					
II B	Control of Communicable Diseases		a	b	⟶				11		
II C	Provisions for Emergencies		a	b	⟶						
II D	Promoting Heathful and Safe School Living		a	b	c	d	⟶				
IV	General Evaluation of School Health and Safety Measures		a	b	c	⟶			3		

* Number of evaluations minus number marked MN or N.
** Transfer to Section Y—appropriate area.

Total   21

I. School Plant

Division	Title of Division	Page	Evaluations						Divisor*	Total	Average**
I. The Site											
I A	Location		*a*	*b*	*c*	⟶			8		
I B	Physical Characteristics		*a*	*b*	*c*	*d*	*e*	⟶			
II. The Building or Buildings			*a*	*b*	*c*	*d*	*e*	*f*	6		
III. Building Services											
III A	Illumination		*a*	*b*	*c*	⟶					
III B	Temperature and Ventilation		*a*	*b*	*c*	⟶			16		
III C	Water and Ventilation		*a*	*b*	*c*	*d*	*e*	*f*			
III D	Miscellaneous Building Services		*a*	*b*	*c*	*d*	⟶				
IV. Classrooms			*a*	*b*	*c*	*d*	⟶		4		
V. Special Rooms and Services											
V A	Auditorium		*a*	*b*	*c*	*d*	⟶				
V B	Gymnasium		*a*	*b*	*c*	*d*	*e*	⟶			
V C	Cafeteria Facilities		*a*	*b*	*c*	*d*	*e*	*f*	25		
V D	Instructional Materials Center		*a*	*b*	*c*	*d*	⟶				
V E	Office and Staff Rooms		*a*	*b*	*c*	*d*	⟶				
V F	Clinic or Health Room		*a*	*b*	⟶						
VI. School Buses			*a*	*b*	*c*	⟶			3		
VII. General Evaluation			*a*	*b*	*c*	⟶			3		░░░
							Total		65		

* Number of evaluations minus number marked MN or N.
** Transfer to Section Y—appropriate area.

J. Administration and School Staff

Division	Title of Division	Page	Evaluations						Divisor*	Total	Average**
I. School Staff											
I-A	Numerical Adequacy		a	b	c	d	e	f	6		
I-B. Administrative Staff											
I-B-1	School Board		a	b	c	————————→					
I-B-2	Superintendent		a	b	c	d	————→				
I-B-3a	Supervisor Preparation—Qualifications		a	b	c	————————→					
I-B-3b	Supervisor—Duties and Functions		a	b	c	————————→			24		
I-B-4	Pastor		a	b	c	————————→					
I-B-5a	Principal—Preparation and Qualifications		a	b	c	————————→					
I-B-5b	Principal—Duties and Functions		a	b	c	d	e	——→			
I-C. Instructional Staff											
I-C-1	Selection of Staff Members		a	b	————————→						
I-C-2	Experience and Length of Service		a	b	————————→						
I-C-3	Improvement		a	b	c	————→			13		
I-C-4	Teaching Load Policy		a	b	c	————→					
I-C-5	Tenure, Leaves of Absence, etc.		a	b	c	————→					
I-D. Noninstructional Staffs											
I-D-1	Secretarial Staff		a	b	c	————→					
I-D-2	Custodial and Maintenance Staff		a	b	c	d	——→		10		
I-D-3	Health and Medical Staff		a	b	c	————→					
II. Organization and Management											
II-A	Pupil Accounting		a	b	————————→						
II-B	Reports to Parents		a	b	c	————→					
II-C	School Finance		————————————→								
II-D	School Schedule		a	b	c	————→			17		
II-E	Maintenance and Operation of plant		a	b	c	————→					
II-F	Lunchrooms, Dining Rooms and Kitchen		a	b	c	————→					
II-G	Transportation of Students		a	b	c	————→					
III. Community Relations											
III-A	Providing Information		a	b	————————→						
III-B	Community Services		a	b	————————→			8		
III-C	Procedures		a	b	c	d	——→				
IV. General Evaluation of the School Staff and Administration			a	b	c	————→			3		░░░░
								Total	81		

* Number of evaluations minus number marked MN or N.
** Transfer to Section Y—appropriate area.

CRITERIA FOR EVALUATION
OF
CATHOLIC ELEMENTARY SCHOOLS, 1965

Formulated and Edited by the Criteria Committee, Elementary School
Department of The National Catholic Educational Association

Graphic Summary

FORM A

	Poor 1	Fair 2	Good 3	Very Good 4	Excellent 5
D—Program of Studies					
D1–D10—Subject Fields					
I. Organization					
II. Nature of Offerings					
III. Physical Facilities					
IV-A. Instructional Staff					
IV-B. Instructional Activities					
IV-C. Instructional Materials					
IV-D. Methods of Evaluation					
V. Outcomes					
VII. General Evaluation of Instruction					
E—Student Activity Program					
F—Instructional Materials Services Library and Multi-Sensory Aids					
G—Guidance Services					
H—Health and Safety Services					
I—School Plant					
J—Administration and School Staff					

Name of School   (Arch)Diocese

Address   City   State

Date of Evaluation   Evaluation Coordinator

General Statement

The "Graphic Summaries" for the *CRITERIA FOR EVALUA-TION OF CATHOLIC ELEMENTARY SCHOOLS* (1965) are indicated as horizontal bar graphs. The school's position on each graph is determined by securing the arithmetic mean of the number of evaluations in the particular section studied. These averages are obtained from Section X, "Statistical Summary," and extend from 1.0 to 5.0.

The number of evaluations for Graphic Summary FORM A and the page numbers in the *CRITERIA* for these evaluations are listed below. In each subdivision D1–10, indicated below, the number of evaluations shown is the greatest possible number, but the actual number for a particular school will depend on the number of subject fields offered.

FORM A

D—*Program of Studies*
    Based on 31 evaluations (Section D, Pp. 29-30; 34-38).

D1–D10—*Subject Fields*
    I. *Organization*
        Based on a possible 44 evaluations (See "I. Organization" of each of subsections D-1 through D-10).

    II. *Nature of Offerings*
        Based on a possible 54 evaluations (See "II. Nature of Offerings" of each of subsections D-1 through D-10).

    III. *Physical Facilities*
        Based on a possible 33 evaluations (See "III. Physical Facilities" of each of subsections D-1 through D-10).

    IV-A. *Instructional Staff*
        Based on a possible 36 evaluations (See "IV-A. Instructional Staff" of each of subsections D-1 through D-10).

    IV-B. *Instructional Activities*
        Based on a possible 43 evaluations (See "IV-B. Instructional Activities" of each of subsections D-1 through D-10).

    IV-C. *Instructional Materials*
        Based on a possible 36 evaluations (See "IV-C. Instructional Materials" of each of subsections D-1 through D-10).

    IV-D. *Methods of Evaluation*
        Based on a possible 36 evaluations (See "IV-D. Methods of Evaluation" of each of subsections D-1 through D-10).

    V. *Outcomes*
        Based on a possible 87 evaluations (See "V. Outcomes" of each of subsections D-1 through D-10).

    VII. *General Evaluation of the Subject Fields*
        Based on a possible 32 evaluations (See "VII. General Evaluations of Instruction in [name of subject field]" of each of subsections D-1 through D-10).

E—*Student Activity Program*
    Based on 22 evaluations (Section E, Pp. 139-144).

F—*Instructional Materials—Library and Multi-Sensory Aids*
    Based on 77 evaluations (Section F, Pp. 147-160).

G—*Guidance Services*
    Based on 16 evaluations (Section G, Pp. 163-167).

H—*Health and Safety Services*
    Based on 21 evaluations (Section H, Pp. 171-176).

I—*School Plant*
    Based on 62 evaluations (Section I, Pp. 179-191).

J—*Administration and School Staff*
    Based on 81 evaluations (Section J, Pp. 196-202; 204-218).

The number of evaluation for Graphic Summary FORM B and the page numbers in the *CRITERIA* of these evaluations are noted below.

D—*Program of Studies*

    I. *Organization*
        Based on 4 evaluations, p. 29.

    II. *Curriculum Development Procedures*
        Based on 4 evaluations, p. 30.

    III. *Subject Offerings*
        Based on 18 evaluations, Pp. 34-37.

    IV. *General Outcomes*
        Based on 2 evaluations, p. 38.

D-1–D-10—*Subject Fields*

D- 1   *Art*
        Based on 33 evaluations, Pp. 43-49.

D- 2—*English Language Arts*
        Based on 47 evaluations, Pp. 53; 56-62.

D- 3   *Foreign Languages*
        Based on 34 evaluations, Pp. 65-72.

D- 4   *Geography*
        Based on 41 evaluations, Pp. 75-80.

D- 5   *Health and Physical Education*
        Based on 47 evaluations, Pp. 83-90.

D- 6   *History*
        Based on 33 evaluations, Pp. 93-98.

D- 7   *Mathematics*
        Based on 36 evaluations, Pp. 101-108.

D- 8   *Music*
        Based on 35 evaluations, Pp. 111-116.

D- 9   *Religion*
        Based on 52 evaluations, Pp. 119-125.

D-10   *Science*
        Based on 43 evaluations, Pp. 130-136.

FORM B

	Poor 1		Fair 2		Good 3		Very Good 4		Excellent 5

D—Program of Studies

I. Organization.............................

II. Curriculum Development Procedures.

III. Subject Offerings.....................

IV. General Outcomes...................

D1—D10—Subject Fields

D- 1 Art.......................................

D- 2 English Language Arts.............

D- 3 Foreign Languages.................

D- 4 Geography............................

D- 5 Health and Physical Education.....

D- 6 History.................................

D- 7 Mathematics.........................

D- 8 Music..................................

D- 9 Religion...............................

D-10 Science...............................

E—*Student Activity Program*

　I.　*General Organization and Nature*

　　　Based on 7 evaluations, Pp. 139-140.

　II.　*Service Activities*

　　　Based on 2 evaluations, p. 141.

　III.　*Creative Activities*

　　　Based on 4 evaluations, p. 142.

　IV.　*Physical Activities*

　　　Based on 6 evaluations, p. 143.

F—*Instructional Materials Services—Library and
Multi-Sensory Aids*

　I.　*Instructional Materials Staff*

　　　Based on 18 evaluations, Pp. 147-149.

　II.　*Organization and Management*

　　　Based on 17 evaluations, Pp. 150-153.

　III.　*Materials*

　　　Based on 29 evaluations, Pp. 154-156.

　IV.　*Physical Facilities*

　　　Based on 9 evaluations, Pp. 157-159.

G—*Guidance Services*

　I.　*General Organization and Nature*

　　　Based on 2 evaluations, p. 163.

　II.　*Guidance Staff*

　　　Based on 2 evaluations, p. 164.

　III.　*Guidance Services*

　　　Based on 9 evaluations, Pp. 165-166.

	Poor 1		Fair 2		Good 3		Very Good 4		Excellent 5

E—Student Activity Program

    I. General Organization and Nature....

    II. Service Activities..............

    III. Creative Activities...........

    IV. Physical Activities...........

F—Instructional Materials Services—
Library and Multi-Sensory Aids

    I. Instructional Materials Staff.........

    II. Organization and Management.......

    III. Materials......................

    IV. Physical Facilities.............

G—Guidance Services

    I. General Organization and Nature....

    II. Guidance Staff.................

    III. Guidance Services.............

	Poor 1	Fair 2	Good 3	Very Good 4	Excellent 5

H—Health and Safety Services

I. General Nature and Organization....

II. School Health Services............

I—School Plant

I. The Site........................

II. The Building or Buildings..........

III. Building Services................

IV. Classrooms....................

V. Special Rooms and Services........

VI. School Buses...................

J—Administration and School Staff...........

I-A. Numerical Adequacy..............

I-B. Administrative Staff..............

I-C. Instructional Staff...............

I-D. Noninstructional Staff............

II. Organization and Management.......

III. Community Relations..............